ULTRASTRUCTURE
OF
PROTEIN FIBERS

ULTRASTRUCTURE
OF
PROTEIN FIBERS

*Papers presented at a symposium of the nine-
teenth annual meeting of the Electron Microscope
Society of America, at the Pittsburgh Hilton Hotel,
Pittsburgh, Pennsylvania, on August 21, 1961*

Edited by

RUBIN BORASKY

Electron Microscope Laboratory
The Graduate College
University of Illinois, Urbana, Illinois

1963

A C A D E M I C   P R E S S   *New York and London*

ACADEMIC PRESS INC.
111 Fifth Avenue, New York 3, New York

United Kingdom Edition published by
ACADEMIC PRESS INC. (LONDON) LTD.
Berkeley Square House, London W.1

LIBRARY OF CONGRESS CATALOG CARD NUMBER: 63-15848

PRINTED IN THE UNITED STATES OF AMERICA

Contributors

RUBIN BORASKY, *Electron Microscope Laboratory, The Graduate College, University of Illinois, Urbana, Illinois*

EMIL BORYSKO, *Ethicon, Inc., Somerville, New Jersey*

ALFRED E. BROWN, *Harris Research Laboratories, Inc., Washington, D.C.*

B. K. FILSHIE, *Division of Protein Chemistry, Wool Research Laboratories, C.S.I.R.O., Melbourne, Australia*

WILLIAM H. JOHNSON, *Department of Physiology, University of Illinois, Urbana, Illinois*[*]

HAROLD P. LUNDGREN, *Western Utilization Research and Development Division, Agricultural Research Service, United States Department of Agriculture, Albany, California*

JOHN MENKART, *Harris Research Laboratories, Inc., Washington, D.C.*

G. E. ROGERS, *Division of Protein Chemistry, Wool Research Laboratories, C.S.I.R.O., Melbourne, Australia*

WILFRED H. WARD, *Western Utilization Research and Development Division, Agricultural Research Service, United States Department of Agriculture, Albany, California*

---

[*] Present address: Department of Biology, Rensselaer Polytechnic Institute, Troy, New York.

v

Preface

"Ultrastructure of Protein Fibers" is the title of a symposium presented at the nineteenth annual meeting of the Electron Microscope Society of America, Pittsburgh, Pennsylvania, August 21, 1961. The symposium had two objectives. One was to discuss the recent advances of knowledge of protein fiber ultrastructure. The second was to disseminate this information to investigators representing a wide diversity of research and development interests in protein fibers. Publishing the symposium in book form preserves the essence of the meeting—namely, that characteristic properties of protein fibers are dependent on the ultrastructure and spatial arrangement of the chemical constituents of which the protein fibers are composed.

The papers "Physical, Chemical, and Mechanical Properties of Protein Fibers" by A. E. Brown and J. Menkart, and "Collagen" by E. Borysko are printed as originally presented at the meeting in Pittsburgh. The papers "The Keratins" by H. P. Lundgren and W. H. Ward, and "Some Aspects of the Ultrastructure of α-Keratin, Bacterial Flagella, and Feather Keratin" by G. E. Rogers and B. K. Filshie were presented as one paper at the meeting. Both of these papers have been revised and enlarged by the authors for this publication. The latter two papers therefore serve as a comprehensive review on the ultrastructure of keratins. The final paper "Fibrous Protein Systems in Muscle" by W. H. Johnson was also revised and enlarged for this publication. This paper serves as a review of a new concept of muscle contraction involving paramyosin and tropomyosin.

The editor is greatly indebted to each of the contributors for the privilege of presenting their work in this form. Grateful acknowledgment is made to Mrs. Olive L. Stayton for her invaluable assistance in preparing the manuscript for publication. Gratitude is expressed to all the authors and publishers for permission to reproduce unpublished and copyrighted original material, relevant sources being given in the bibliographies and indicated appropriately in the text. Finally, the editor expresses many thanks to Academic Press for their helpful suggestions and cooperation in the publication of this volume.

RUBIN BORASKY

February, 1963
Urbana, Illinois

Contents

List of Illustrations

xi

THE KERATINS

HAROLD P. LUNDGREN AND WILFRED H. WARD

SOME ASPECTS OF THE ULTRASTRUCTURE OF α-KERATIN, BACTERIAL FLAGELLA, AND FEATHER KERATIN

G. E. ROGERS AND B. K. FILSHIE

FIBROUS PROTEIN SYSTEMS IN MUSCLE

William H. Johnson

List of Tables

Introduction: Some Important Aspects of Protein Fiber Research

RUBIN BORASKY

Electron Microscope Laboratory, The Graduate College
University of Illinois
Urbana, Illinois

Research on the ultrastructure of fibrous proteins has three important objectives. They are (1) to elucidate the fundamental ultra-architecture of proteins in general, (2) to determine the biological role played by fibrous proteins in living organisms, and (3) to make the most efficient use of protein fibers as a natural resource in the form of raw materials and finished products. All of these aspects are intimately associated with the ultrastructure or ultra-architecture of protein fiber macromolecules that are the basic structural units of organelles, tissues, organs, and secretions of living organisms. The purpose of this introduction is to discuss briefly some important aspects of protein fiber research as a general preview of the papers to be presented in this symposium.

Proteins may be empirically classified into two kinds—the globular and the fibrous proteins. The basic structural units of protein macromolecules are polypeptide strands. In the globular proteins the polypeptide strands are so folded and misaligned one with another, that the macromolecules appear to be spherical. There seems to be little ordered or oriented structure. Such proteins do not make good subjects for determination or study of ultra-architecture of proteins. In the fibrous proteins, however, the polypeptide strands if folded may be ascertained by means of x-ray and electronoscopic analysis. The structure is ordered and may manifest itself as axial periodicity, lateral association, and preferred or definitive alignment of the polypeptide chains to form filaments, fibrils,

1

and fibers. Thus fibrous proteins are fair to excellent subjects for the study of protein ultrastructure. Much of our present fundamental knowledge of protein ultrastructure is based on studies of fibrous proteins and will be discussed by the contributors to this volume.

Fibrous proteins play a very important role in biological function and structure. Motility in micro-organisms and higher animal forms is associated with organelles (cilia, fimbria, flagella, *et al.*), tissues (muscle and skeletal), and organs chiefly constituted of fibrous proteins. Protective tissues and structures, e.g., skin, scales, cuticles, feathers, nails, *et al.*, are constituted of fibrous proteins or are laid down on a matrix of protein fibers. The great bulk of the organic constituents of vertebrate and many invertebrate animals is fibrous proteins. In fact, fibrous proteins have been termed structure proteins. This designation suggests that fibrous proteins are relatively inert and have no biological function other than mechanical, supportive, or protective. Such ideas are far from the actualities. Fibrous proteins have a very important physiological role—in energy transformations, water balance, and respiration. The physiological characteristics are also intimately associated with fine structure or ultra-architecture of protein fibers. How else can one account for the binding of water, the contraction of muscle, the elasticity of tendon and skin, and other such phenomena than on a 3-dimensional ultrastructure?

The third reason for studying protein fiber ultrastructure is the fact that fibrous proteins form the basis for a tremendous industrial and economic complex. Collagen is the principal raw material for the leather, gelatin, and animal glue industry. The annual monetary value of the collagen-based industrial complex is about 4 billion dollars. Keratins in the form of hair, wool, and bristles are the raw materials for an industrial complex that includes textiles, carpets, brushes, upholstery stuffing, and beauty aids worth more than 1.5 billion dollars annually. In 1958 the bill for beautifying milady's hair was more than 61 million dollars. These values are for the United States alone. World production of raw silk was valued at about 500 thousand dollars in 1959. The muscle-based industry—meat production—is valued about 16 billion dollars a year.

All in all the industrial complex based on collagen, keratin, and silk fibroin and muscle is valued at much more than 21.5 billion dollars annually. This in itself is a worthy motive for learning as much as we can about the ultrastructure of protein fibers.[1]

It is interesting to note that fibrous proteins as a basis for the industrial complex described above have functions for the finished product similar to those in the living organisms, i.e., mechanical support, protection, and as a source of energy.

As is noted above protein fiber research has many facets, each of which could well be the theme for unlimited discussion. However, the time allocated for this symposium is limited to one afternoon (3 hours). Because of this time limitation the symposium is organized to attain the following two objectives: (1) to provide the audience with information on the most recent advances in our knowledge on protein fiber ultrastructure, and (2) to provide a general perspective of the similarities and differences of protein fiber properties as related to their ultra-architecture. It is felt that these objectives could best be attained by discussing first the physical, chemical, and mechanical properties of protein fibers, and following this with three specific kinds of fibrous proteins, collagen and keratin and muscle. Collagen, keratin, and muscle were chosen for special emphasis because these three protein genera are probably the most exhaustively studied of the fibrous proteins and much of our knowledge of protein ultrastructure is based on these studies. The emphasis on collagen, keratin, and muscle does not preclude consideration of other fibrous proteins such as silk, synthetic protein fibers, and the protein from bacterial flagella, as will be seen in the following papers.

---

[1] U.S. Bureau of Census and Manufactures (1958), Census of Business (1958), Bureau of the Census, Washington, D.C.

Physical, Chemical, and Mechanical Properties of Protein Fibers

Alfred E. Brown and John Menkart

Harris Research Laboratories, Inc., Washington, D.C.

The protein fibers form a class of their own, in contrast with other organic natural and synthetic fibers, in two important aspects of behavior: (1) their mechanical properties, particularly their long-range elasticity; and (2) their high moisture-sorbing capacity. These two characteristics are important not only for the use of fibrous proteins as textile materials, but also for their functions in biological systems. The relationship of these physical and mechanical properties to the chemical composition and molecular structure of the protein fibers forms the main theme of this paper.

The fibrous proteins fall into four groups differing in the arrangement of their polypeptide chains:

(a) The α-helix coil, found in wool keratin, epidermin, myosin, fibrinogen (*18, 21*). The ability of this coiled configuration to be stretched out to about double its normal length confers to these materials their unusual long-range extensibility and elasticity.

(b) The extended "pleated sheet" configuration typified by silk fibroin and the β-keratin of feathers or of stretched wool (*13, 16*). Strength and low extensibility are the characteristics of the fibers in this group.

(c) The special case of the collagens, in which the molecular organization is apparently based on a group of three polypeptide chains, each a left-hand helix, wound together in a shallow-pitch right-hand helix (*1, 10, 19*). The resulting structure, held together by strong hydrogen bonds, has relatively little extensibility, but collapses readily into a much shorter configuration when interchain bonding is disrupted.

(d) The random coil, obtained by denaturation of globular proteins, which can be transformed into the extended β configuration by drawing (15); all the regenerated protein fibers (peanut, zein, casein, egg albumin) fall in this category.

It is of interest to note in passing that synthetic polypeptides have been prepared in the α-helix, in the pleated sheet configuration, and some even in an approximation to the complicated collagen structure. Studies on such polypeptides have, indeed, thrown much light on the structure of the more complex natural proteins.[1]

The most common protein fibers, wool and silk, belong in somewhat different categories in respect to mechanical properties, wool being characterized by long-range extensibility, great elasticity, and moderately low strength, whereas silk possesses much greater strength but a lower extensibility. The basis for this difference in behavior is found in the nature and structural arrangement of the molecules of the two types of proteins.

Information on the structure of silk has increased enormously during the past decade, particularly in understanding relationships between amino acid composition and sequence along the chain, the structural arrangements among chains, and the mechanical properties of the resultant fibers (13).

The polypeptide chain of fibroin, the protein of silk, is composed of alternating segments which differ substantially in their composition. One segment consists entirely of the amino acids with short side chains—glycine, alanine, and serine—in the molar proportions of 3:2:1. The basic design of this segment is described by a hexapeptide containing these three amino acids in the sequence (Gly.Ser.Gly.Ala.Gly.Ala.), repeated to give about 60 residues (12). This simple pattern apparently represents the crystalline part of the structure. The other segment, which corresponds to the amorphous portion, has a more complicated composition, containing, besides the three above amino acids, all the other ones with bulkier side chains; prominent among these are tyrosine, arginine, valine, aspartic acid, and glutamic acid. Little is known about the residue sequence in this portion of the molecule, though

[1] Helical configuration of the polymer chain has recently been observed in other polymers also; for example, in polytetrafluoroethylene (6).

there is some evidence to indicate, for example, that the tyrosine is regularly spaced through the structure.

In the fibroin of *Bombyx mori*, the silk of commerce, the molecule of some 1100 residues consists of 12 of the "simple" segments of about 60 residues each, alternating with the "complex" sections of about 33 residues each.

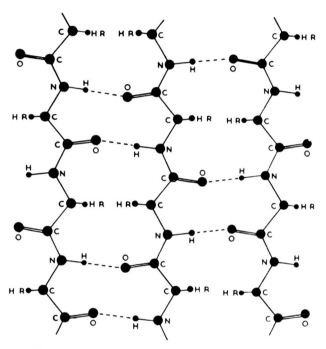

FIG. 1. Fully extended polypeptide chains with the sequence NH·CHR·CO running in opposite directions in adjacent chains (antiparallel pleated sheet). From Bamford *et al.* (2).

The chains are in the extended, "antiparallel pleated sheet" (7) configuration (Fig. 1). In the "simple," crystalline segment, the bulkier side chains (methyl in alanine, hydroxymethyl in serine) occur in every second residue, and thus project on one side of the sheet. The sheets are arranged back-to-back, which permits the very compact arrangement illustrated in Fig. 2.

This close packing, which favors the formation of strong hydrogen bonds between the peptide groups of neighboring chains, confers to silk its high strength in both the dry and the wet states. The extensibility of the fiber is based on the mobility of the chains in the amorphous regions of the structure.

In *Bombyx mori* silk, about 87% of the residues are derived from amino acids with short side chains; on the basis of the molecular model, this means that about 60% of the silk fibroin is in the crystalline form. The proportion of the short side-chain amino acids present varies from one species of silk to another. Lucas *et al.*

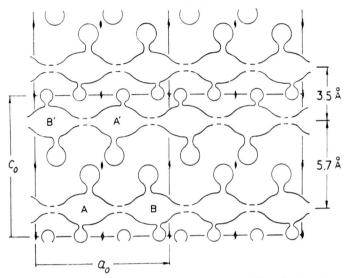

FIG. 2. Diagrammatic cross section of the assembly of the polypeptide chains in *Bombyx mori* fibroin (*16*).

(*11*) have studied silks from three families of silkworms; they obtained the values given in the tabulation.

	Short-chain amino acids (%)
Anaphe moloneyi	95.2
Bombyx mori	87.4
Antherea mylitta	71.1

It is instructive to examine how these differences in composition —and consequently in crystallinity—are reflected in the mechanical properties of the fibers. The stress-strain curves for the three fibers, in a standard atmosphere of 65% relative humidity (R.H.), 70°C, are shown in Fig. 3. The highly crystalline *Anaphe* silk has a linear stress-strain curve up to the breaking point, with a low extension, 12½%, at a breaking load of 5 gm per denier. The greater proportion of amorphous material in the *Bombyx* structure causes a substantial increase in extensibility, the breaking extension

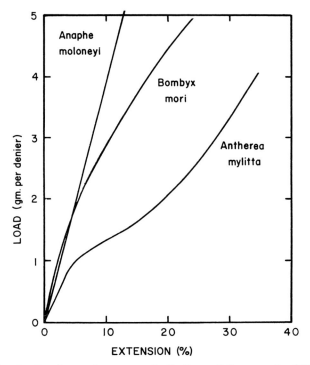

FIG. 3.   Load-extension curves of silk fibers of three species (*11*).

being 24%. When the crystallinity is still further decreased, as in the *Antherea* silk, the extensibility increases even more, up to 35%, and the stress-strain curve begins to exhibit the characteristics associated with wool keratin—a yield point at an extension of about 5%, followed by flow and then by a hardening, which may be ascribed to the reinforcement of the fiber resulting from orientation of the amorphous regions.

Interestingly, the moisture regain at 65% differs very little from one silk fiber to another, which suggests that the peptide groups play a predominant part in the sorption of water, and hydrophilic side chains a less important one (*14, 17*). It also shows that the differences in stress-strain behavior at 65% R.H. just discussed are truly a function of molecular organization, and not just a reflection of plasticization by sorbed water. However, when the fibers are immersed in liquid water, the amorphous portion of the structure becomes plasticized, whereas the crystalline region is unaffected. Consequently, the effect of water on the extensibility of the fiber increases as the crystallinity decreases:

	Extension at 0.5 gm/ denier: in water at 65% R.H.
Anaphe moloneyi	1.3
Bombyx mori	2.5
Antherea mylitta	4.4

Elastic recovery from deformation also varies with the crystallinity:

	% Elastic recovery from a 10% extension	
	In air	In water
Anaphe moloneyi	50	50
Bombyx mori	50	60
Antherea mylitta	30	70

The more amorphous structures recover poorly from deformation in the air-dry state, due to interactions between the bulky side chains. When these interactions are reduced by the presence of water, the recovery is improved; in the highly crystalline *Anaphe* fiber, the recovery is unaffected by the presence of water.

This brief discussion shows that, in the case of silk, the molecular structure is well understood, and much of the mechanical behavior of the fiber is explicable in the light of this structural picture. The other well-known protein fiber, wool, is being discussed in detail in other papers at this Symposium, and it is mentioned here merely to contrast its structure with that of silk.

Wool is extremely complex morphologically, and also chemically, being composed of a mixture of proteins. It is therefore not surprising that such precise information on molecular structure and arrangement which has emerged for silk during the past six to seven years is not yet available for wool. The more general picture which we have does, however, enable us to pick out the significant differences between the two types of structure. Compared to silk, the proportion of low molecular weight amino acids in wool is very small, approximately 20%. Practically all of the amino acids have large, bulky side chains. Analytical data, shown in Table I, show that wool is, in comparison with silk, deficient in glycine, alanine, and serine, and rich in aspartic acid, glutamic acid, arginine, proline, and cystine.

TABLE I

AMINO ACID COMPOSITION OF SILK, WOOL, AND ZEIN[a]

Amino acid	Silk (12) (Bombyx mori)	Merino 64's wool (20)	Zein (4)
Glycine	43.7	5.8	0
Alanine	28.7	3.5	11.2
Valine	2.2	3.6	2.2
Leucine	0.5	4.9	25.9
Isoleucine	0.7	2.0	4.9
Serine	11.9	7.3	6.4
Threonine	0.9	4.6	2.2
Aspartic acid	1.3	4.2	3.7
Glutamic acid	1.0	8.6	15.9
Phenylalanine	0.6	1.8	3.4
Tyrosine	5.1	3.0	2.5
Lysine	0.6	3.3	0
Histidine	0.5	1.5	1.9
Arginine	1.8	20.3	3.6
Proline	0.4	5.3	7.9
Tryptophan	0.3	1.7	0
Methionine	0.1	0.3	5.6
Cystine	—	7.9	0.7
Amide N	0	7.5	14.8

[a] Amino acid N as a percentage of total N.

Such a structure cannot form the extended, pleated sheet pattern. Instead, the molecules are coiled, largely in the α-helix pattern (8, 18) (Fig. 4). Though polypeptide chains in the helical coil can aggregate into crystal structures, this happens to a very limited extent in wool. Most of the coiled chains are arranged in an amorphous, and consequently very flexible, arrangement.

With this molecular picture, the long-range elasticity of wool is easily explained. The long, flexible chains which exist in coiled configurations (α-keratin), on stretching open to the more fully extended chain configuration (β-keratin); the process is reversible.

Modern polymer chemistry predicts that a fiber made up of coiled chains should have very low strength. It can be demonstrated that this would be the case with wool were it not for its unique molecular structure due to the presence of covalent disulfide links between the main polypeptide chains. These disulfide cross links result from the high cystine content of wool (Table I). Therefore, when

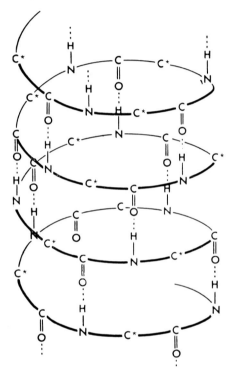

Fig. 4.   The α-helix coil (schematic). From Bamford *et al.* (2).

wool is subjected to various types of strain, the chains cannot slide past one another, but instead, tensions are set up by the cross links which act as restoring forces so that the fiber returns to its original configuration on removal of the load. The cross links have the all-important function of strengthening the fiber, particularly in the wet state.

It is evident that at least two distinct molecular models are available as patterns for the preparation of synthetic fiber from proteins. They are the "silk model" and the "wool model." The former requires molecules which can be readily straightened and are made up of monomeric units such that a major part of the segments of the molecules are able to fit into crystalline areas, whereas a limited portion of the segments contain bulky side chains which give rise to amorphous regions. By anchoring the chains in the crystalline areas, the strength, and more especially, wet strength, remains high; the amorphous regions make possible chain mobility which accounts for a limited range of extensibility and elasticity. The "wool model" requires chains which do not crystallize and so tend to be more or less folded or coiled; in this case, the chains must be anchored at intervals by covalent cross links to supply sufficient strength. Which of the two natural fiber models is approached in actual practice depends on the chemical structure of the protein, the ease with which the molecules are transformed from their natural configurations to an optimum configuration for fiber construction, and the extent to which the desirable configuration can be stabilized.

With this understanding, we can consider the efforts of the synthetic fiber industry directed to the production of fibers from various proteins in order to simulate the desirable properties of wool and silk. Thus, fibers have been spun from casein, soya bean, peanut, zein, collagen, chicken-feather keratin, egg albumin, gliadin, and blood serum proteins (15). Although there has been much progress, commercial success has remained elusive.

Chemical analysis of proteins which are economically suitable for conversion into fibers quickly indicates that they are all similar to wool, rather than to silk, in that they are composed largely of amino acids with bulky side chains. A typical example, zein, is given in Table I. This indicates that the possibility of fabricating from these materials a structure based on the "silk model" is remote, and this has been found to be the case.[2]

The manipulation of protein molecules into fibrous form is not simple. Most native proteins have folded structures which are unsuitable for fiber formation. The problem is one of transforming

---

[2] The production of a satisfactory "silk model" fiber is difficult, even when the problem of composition, due to the bulky side chains, is absent. Attempts to produce a useful fiber by regenerating silk itself have so far met with failure. It is apparently difficult to achieve *in vitro* the perfect organization of the polypeptide chains which the silkworm attains when it extrudes the filament from its silk gland (22).

these highly folded configurations into an extended state in order to construct fibers with desirable mechanical properties. Fortunately, protein denaturation makes this possible. Many agents, notably alkali and swelling agents such as urea or guanidine salts, denature the protein and tend to keep the molecules more or less fully extended (23).

Because of the bulky side-chain structures, which prevent crystallization in pleated sheets, the stabilization of these protein chains

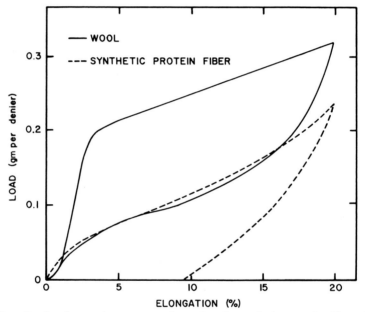

Fig. 5. Load-extension curves of wool and synthetic protein fibers in water (9).

to produce fibers cannot be achieved simply by anchoring large portions of the chains in crystalline regions, as is done in silk; other forms of stabilization are needed. One form of stabilization, covalent cross-linking as it exists in wool, has already been mentioned. Since some native proteins also swell enormously in water, and even dissolve, means for diminishing their affinity for water by converting hydrophilic into hydrophobic groups can be considered a second form of stabilization (5). In practice, both types of chemical treatment have been used. Reaction with formaldehyde is widely used for cross-linking, and increased wet strength is

obtained (3). Typical of the second type of treatment is acetyla-
tion, or treatment with heavy metal salts, such as aluminum or
mercury salts. Marked resistance of the fiber to the deleterious
swelling and softening action of hot water is obtained in this way.

The problem of attaining adequate wet strength in synthetic
protein fibers has not been completely solved, and this is perhaps
the biggest barrier to their widespread use. The nature of the
problem is readily seen by comparing the mechanical properties

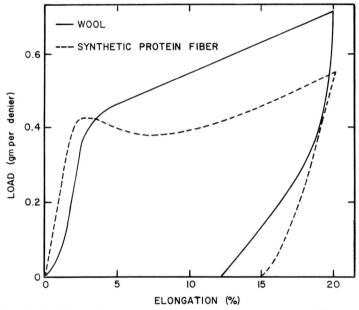

Fig. 6.   Load-extension curves of wool and synthetic protein fiber in air
at 65% R.H. (9).

of a synthetic protein fiber, such as zein, with those of wool. Typical stress-strain curves are given in Figs. 5 and 6. The fibers are
stretched 20% of their original length, and allowed to contract
after the removal of the load. The striking feature of the curves is
the similarity in behavior of the two fibers when dry, in contrast
with the wide difference between them when wet. The secondary
and covalent bonding between the polypeptide chains of the dry
synthetic protein fiber is sufficient to produce strength and elasticity comparable to wool. In the wet state, on the other hand,
the effectiveness of the secondary bonding is reduced, and the

lack of good covalent bonding, such as is present in wool, becomes manifest.

The role of the disulfide cross linkages in the wet mechanical properties of wool is demonstrated by the fact that the rupture of a significant portion of these linkages produces a fiber which has the weaker wet mechanical properties of synthetic protein fibers (9). By analogy, therefore, it appears that the development of outstanding protein fibers with properties similar to those of wool awaits the development of *more effective* cross-linking techniques. The problem cannot be solved by simply increasing the number of formaldehyde cross linkages, for example, because in this way a brittle, inextensible fiber is produced.

Although most participants in this Symposium are interested in protein fibers from various points of view, probably few have been as concerned with their structure and properties as have those of us who consider them as textile materials. Indeed, at first glance, textile fibers do not appear to have much in common with proteins such as enzymes, hormones, muscle, tissues, viruses, etc. Yet, on careful consideration of the relationships we have discussed, it is evident that there is much in common among these materials; namely, the types of inter- and intramolecular bonds between peptide chains which maintain their particular structures. These, in turn, influence their chemical, physical, mechanical, and physiological properties, which are of almost universal interest.

REFERENCES

1. Astbury, W. T., *J. Soc. Leather Trades' Chemists* **45**, 186 (1961).
2. Bamford, C. H., Elliot, A., and Hanby, W. E., "Synthetic Polypeptides." Academic Press, New York, 1956.
3. Bjorksten, J., *Advances in Protein Chem.* **6**, 343 (1951).
4. Brohult, S., and Sandegren, E., "The Proteins" (H. Neurath and K. Bailey, eds.), Vol. II, A487. Academic Press, New York, 1954.
5. Brown, A. E., Gordon, W. G., Gall, E. C., and Jackson, R. W., *Ind. Eng. Chem.* **36**, 1171 (1944).
6. Clark, E. S., Starkweather, H. W., Jr., *J. Appl. Polymer. Sci.* **6**, S41 (1962).
7. Corey, R. B., and Pauling, L., *Proc. Roy. Soc.* (*London*) **B141**, 10 (1953).
8. Crick, F. H. C., *Acta Cryst.* **6**, 689 (1953).
9. Harris, M., and Brown, A. E., "Fibrous Proteins," pp. 203-206. Soc. Dyers Colourists, Bradford, England, 1946.
10. Highberger, J. H., *J. Am. Leather Chemists' Assoc.* **54**, 422 (1961).
11. Lucas, F., Shaw, J. T. B., and Smith, S. G., *J. Textile Inst.* **46**, T440 (1955).

12. Lucas, F., Shaw, J. T. B., and Smith, S. G., *Biochem. J.* **66**, 468 (1957).
13. Lucas, F., Shaw, J. T. B., and Smith, S. B., *Advances in Protein Chem.* **13**, 108 (1958).
14. Lucas, F., and Smith, S. G., *J. Textile Inst.* **50**, T695 (1959).
15. Lundgren, H. P., *Advances in Protein Chem.* **5**, 305 (1949).
16. Marsh, R. E., Corey, R. B., and Pauling, L., *Biochim. et Biophys. Acta* **16**, 1 (1955).
17. Mellon, E. F., Korn, A. H., and Hoover, S. R., *J. Am. Chem. Soc.* **70**, 3040 (1948).
18. Pauling, L., and Corey, R. B., *Nature* **171**, 59 (1953).
19. Rich, A., and Crick, F. C. H., *Nature* **176**, 915 (1955).
20. Simmonds, D. H., *Proc. Intern. Wool Textile Research Conf. Australia* **C65** (1955).
21. Skertchly, A., and Woods, H. J., *J. Textile Inst.* **51**, T517 (1960).
22. Wakeham, H., Toner, P. K., Jolley, H. R., and Taylor, H. S., *Textile Research J.* **21**, 110 (1951).
23. Wormell, R. L., "New Fibres from Proteins," p. 48. Academic Press, New York, 1954.

Collagen

EMIL BORYSKO

Ethicon, Inc.
Somerville, New Jersey

The latest and probably most widely accepted theory of the structure of the collagen fibril was developed by the brilliant work and thinking of several of our oldest members—Francis O. Schmitt, Jerome Gross, and Cecil Hall. This theory holds that the fundamental unit of structure of the collagen fibril is a huge macromolecule, the tropocollagen molecule, measuring some 2,800 Å in length by 15 Å in width with a molecular weight approaching 300,000. The tropocollagen molecules are presumed to be produced by fibroblasts as shown diagrammatically in Text Fig. 1. The molecules float about in the extracellular space until some as yet unknown set of environmental circumstances causes them to aggregate laterally and longitudinally to form a collagen fibril exhibiting a typical periodic, cross-banded appearance. According to the current theory, the periodic structure is the result of a precise overlap of one-quarter of the length of the tropocollagen units as they come together, producing a lateral juxtaposition of electron-dense sites. Though the preponderance of evidence supports this theory, no one has yet been able to visualize the arrangement of the tropocollagen units in the electron microscope, even though they are sufficiently large to be resolved in our present-day instruments. This was one of the primary objectives in our research.

Collagen fibrils form a wide variety of patterns in the various tissues of the animal body. In cowhide, for example (Fig. 1), they are grouped into fibers that branch and anastomose to form a complex structure ideally suited to resist the stresses and strains involved in holding together and protecting a ton of cow. This is demonstrated best in a polarizing microscope where the inherent

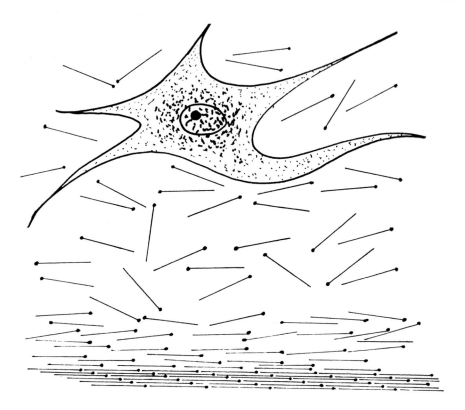

Text Fig. 1. Diagrammatic representation of the tropocollagen theory for the formation of collagen fibrils. Polarized tropocollagen molecules or their precursors are produced by the fibroblasts. They float about in the extra-cellular space and finally aggregate laterally and longitudinally to form collagen fibrils.

Fig. 1. Photomicrograph of a 5-micron section of cowhide as seen in polarized light between crossed polaroids. The collagen fibers are brightest where they are oriented at 45° to the plane of polarization.

Fig. 2. Photomicrograph of a 5-micron section of beef leg tendon as seen in polarized light between crossed polaroids. The relatively uniform brightness indicates that the collagen fibrils are all oriented parallel to the long axis of the tendon.

Fig. 3. Phase-contrast photomicrograph of a dispersion of beef leg tendon collagen fibers in water. This is representative of the wet, unswollen "natural" condition of the fibers. Magnification: 450 ×.

Fig. 4. Phase-contrast photomicrograph of a dispersion of swollen beef leg tendon fibrils in dilute acetic acid. Note the relatively low contrast as compared to the same type of collagen shown in the unswollen state in Fig. 3. Magnification: 990 ×.

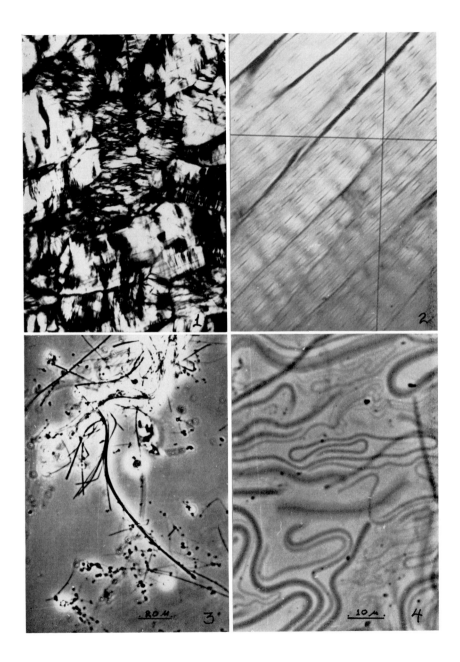

birefringence of the collagen fibrils serves to accentuate the random pattern of the hide fibers. In the hind-leg tendon of the cow (Fig. 2), the collagen fibrils are all oriented parallel to the long axis of the tendon, so that a longitudinal section shows a high order of birefringence when oriented at 45° to the plane of polarization. In other tissues, such as the cornea, the collagen fibrils are arranged in laminated sheets or they may occur as a fine network of individual fibrils holding the soft tissues and glands together. The mechanisms involved in the organization of the collagen fibrils in the tissues are completely unknown, but they are certainly more complex than that proposed by Wilson.[1] I quote: "During the period of growth of an animal, fibroblasts leave the blood streams and migrate outward through the skin, each one exuding collagen material along the path of its travel, the exuded material becoming a single, long fibril. The fibroblast may thus be likened in its action to a silk worm that spins out a long filament or fibril of silk in forming its cocoon."

A good deal of the work leading to the current concept of fibrogenesis and the structure of the collagen fibril was based on experiments with neutral-salt-soluble fractions of various collagenous tissues. This soluble material generally constitutes a very small portion of the total collagen present. Our interest is mainly in the insoluble variety of collagen that goes into the manufacture of

---

[1] J. A. Wilson, "Modern Practice in Leather Manufacture." Reinhold, New York, 1941.

FIG. 5. Phase-contrast photomicrograph of an acid dispersion of short segments of swollen beef leg tendon fibrils. Many of the segments are seen on end, showing the dense central region and the round cross-sectional shape of the fibrils. The lengths of the segments ranged from 3 to 12 microns, averaging about 7 microns. Magnification: 2,070 ×.

FIG. 6. Electron micrograph of a swollen beef leg tendon fibril stained with PTA to show the dense central region. Magnification: 33,750 ×.

FIG. 7. Electron micrograph of one end of a highly swollen beef leg tendon fibril shadowed with chromium at a 4:1 angle, showing the extreme flatness of the fibrils when they dry down on the supporting film. Though the chrome tends to obscure fine detail, it is obvious that there is no fibrillation of the fibril end. The small tendrils extending out from the edges of the fibril are interpreted to be drying artifacts. Magnification: 12,600 ×.

FIG. 8. Portion of a kangaroo tail tendon swollen by immersion in dilute acetic acid for about 24 hours.

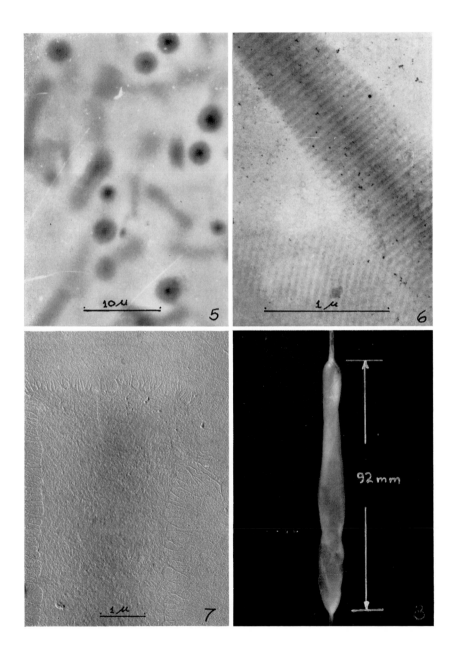

absorbable sutures and other collagen products of medical interest. Therefore most of this report will be concerned with some of the unique physical and morphological characteristics of this type of collagen.

Collagen fibrils are generally too small to be studied with an optical microscope, ranging from about 100 to perhaps 4–5 thousand Å in diameter in the natural wet state. However, most collagen fibrils can be made to swell to many times their original diameters by simply placing them in aqueous acid media. In the swollen state, the collagen fibrils from many tissues are large enough to be studied with an optical microscope. The fibrils from beef leg tendon in the natural, unswollen, wet state, dispersed in water in a Waring blendor, show very little by way of structure (Fig. 3). In such a preparation the fibrils are small in diameter and relatively long, but it is difficult to say whether any one of them is a fibril or a bundle of fibrils, since many broom out and subdivide. If we take the same dispersion of fibrils and add a few drops of acetic acid to depress the pH to less than 4, we get an entirely different picture, as shown in Fig. 4. At low pH, the fibrils swell greatly and become so transparent that they are completely invisible in an ordinary microscope. They must be studied with good phase-contrast optics. The degree of swelling is such that a dispersion containing less than 1% of collagen is almost as viscous and transparent as jelly. In the past, this has misled many workers in the collagen field into believing that such preparations were true gels with a particle size considerably below the limits of resolution of the optical microscope, and certainly very much smaller than the original collagen fibrils. Exactly the reverse is true. In the unswollen state, the maximum fibril diameter of beef leg tendon is less than 0.5 micron. In the swollen state, the minimum fibril diameter is about 0.5 micron with a maximum in excess of 3 microns. Many of the larger fibrils exhibit a distinct dense central region which could be interpreted as an optical artifact. To check this, acid dispersions of 5-micron segments of the fibrils were made. In such dispersions, many short pieces of the fibrils were seen on end, as shown in Fig. 5. The dense central region appears as a dot in the middle of the perfectly round cross section of the fibril, demonstrating beyond a reasonable doubt that the dense region seen in the lateral view of the fibrils was not an optical artifact. We can turn to the electron microscope for additional evidence. Figure 6 shows a

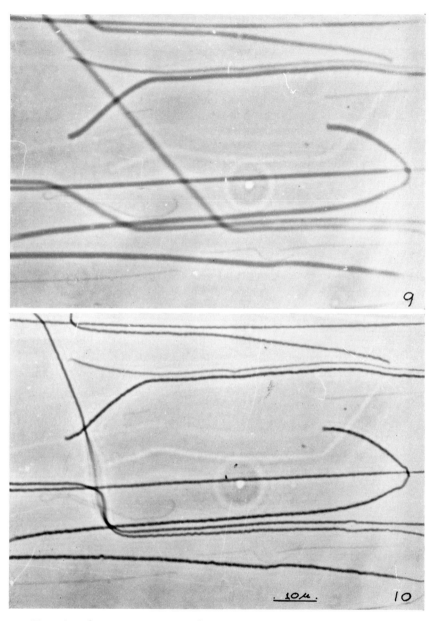

FIGS. 9 and 10. Comparative photomicrographs of collagen fibrils in the swollen and unswollen states. The unswollen fibrils (Fig. 10) are denser and have a kinky appearance but, when measured with a map measure, they are exactly the same length as when they were swollen. The kinky appearance is an artifact caused by a sudden large increase in pH. Magnification: 1,170 ×.

preparation of swollen beef tendon collagen fibrils that had been allowed to dry on a carbon-coated grid and stained with phospho-tungstic acid (PTA). The dense central region is quite apparent. The high electron density of the central region of the fibrils in this picture is not due to their roundness. In shadowed preparations (Fig. 7) one can see that the swollen fibrils flatten out completely when they dry down on the supporting film. The flattened fibrils are insignificantly thin and completely invisible in the electron beam unless they are either heavily stained or shadowed. We prefer to stain since shadowing tends to obscure many fine details.

The acid swelling reaction of the collagens has many interesting facets. When a length of dry kangaroo tail tendon was immersed in an acid medium, it swelled to many times its original diameter as shown in Fig. 8. The tendon was doubled over and placed in an acid medium overnight with the two ends protruding from the surface. The swelling ended abruptly at the surface—there was absolutely no diffusion upward into the dry portions of the tendon, suggesting that the swelling was not a simple matter of filling up the voids in a sponge. Although the swollen tendons increased manyfold in diameter, there was a decrease of about 25% in length. When we fastened one end of an unswollen kangaroo tail tendon to a rod and hooked the other end to a spring balance clamped at the other end of the rod, we found that a force of several hundred grams was developed by the shrinkage that occurred during swelling. The swelling process was completely reversible. By leaching the acid swelling medium out of the tendon with running tap water overnight, the tendon returned to its original dimensions

---

FIG. 11. Electron micrograph of a chrome-shadowed preparation of swollen collagen fibrils, showing localized patches of 640-Å periodicity where the fibrils are highly swollen as well as complete cross bands where de-swelling has occurred at the crossing of the two fibrils. Magnification: 8,820 ×.

FIG. 12. Swollen beef leg tendon fibrils from a 6-month-old dispersion illustrating the effect of aging on these preparations. The fibrils are obviously more highly swollen than in the fresh preparations, as evidenced by their greater transparency and larger average diameters. Quantitative determinations of the degree of swelling confirmed this. Magnification: 1,170 ×.

FIG. 13. Swollen collagen fibrils obtained from the serous layer of beef small intestine, illustrating the small diameter and relative uniformity of the fibrils in this tissue. Magnification: 1,170 ×.

FIG. 14. Swollen collagen fibrils obtained from kangaroo tail tendon. Magnification: 1,170 ×.

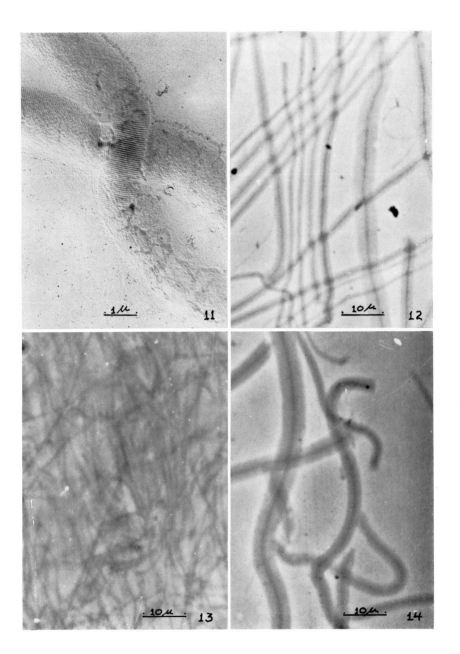

and weight. We swelled and de-swelled a tendon repeatedly for 2 weeks without any apparent change in this property. At the fibril level, however, the swelling presents a somewhat different picture. We found that, in the case of beef leg tendon fibrils, the swelling involves the lateral dimension of the fibrils only. This was done by direct measurements of the same fibrils in the swollen and unswollen states. Figure 9 shows a typical group of swollen collagen fibrils. After taking this picture, the pH of the swelling medium was increased by diffusion of dilute ammonium hydroxide under the coverslip. This caused these fibrils to de-swell so that we were able to get a comparative photograph as shown in Fig. 10. We measured these fibrils before and after de-swelling and found that there was absolutely no change in their lengths, either individually or in aggregate. When swollen beef leg tendon fibrils are examined in the electron microscope, most of them exhibit the standard 640-Å periodicity. However, some of the fibrils are so highly swollen that the 640-Å period disappears. I should remark at this point that the relative degree of swelling of the fibrils could be estimated in both optical and electron microscopes by their transparency—as one could expect, the greater the degree of swelling, the higher the transparency. In many of the highly swollen fibrils, small patches of 640-Å periodicity can still be found as shown in Fig. 11. The retention of the dimensions of the periodic structure provides further evidence that the swelling of the fibrils involves the lateral dimension only.

Though most of the swelling of the fibrils occurs during the first few seconds of immersion in the acid medium, we have discovered that the swelling continues at a low rate over a period of several months. By centrifuging a dispersion at about 100,000 g for 1 hr, the swollen fibrils can be separated from the dispersing fluid. When this was done repeatedly on aliquots of the same dispersion for several months and the per cent fibrils by weight plotted against time, we obtained the curve shown in Text Fig. 2. We suspected this particular property of beef tendon collagen fibrils when we examined a 6-month-old dispersion of swollen fibrils that had been setting in a hidden corner of one of our shelves. In the phase-contrast microscope, the swollen fibrils were obviously larger and more transparent than those we were accustomed to seeing in fresh preparations (Fig. 12). In addition, a much higher percentage of the fibrils in the old sample had dense central cores which may be interpreted to mean that the peripheral portion of the fibrils swells at a greater long-term rate than the central portion. If we could assume that the central region of the fibrils was considerably older than the peripheral zone, the lower swelling rate in the center of the fibril would tend to support the idea expressed by Dr. Gross about the effect of aging on collagen.

One cannot assume from these observations on beef leg tendon fibrils that collagen from other sources reacts in the same manner

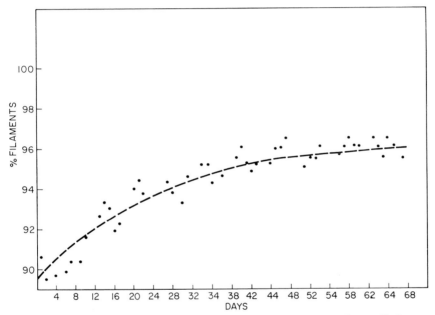

Text Fig. 2.   Long-term swelling curve of beef leg tendon collagen fibrils.

to the acid swelling media. The differences between collagen fibrils from different species or even from different tissues in the same species are much more pronounced than their similarities. It is well known that rat tail tendon fibrils dissolve completely in aqueous acid media, but we have kept kangaroo tail tendon in acid solution for months without any sign of dissolution. Codfish skin collagen forms a good dispersion of swollen fibrils at low temperatures but, when warmed to room temperature, the swollen fibrils degenerate almost completely. I say "almost" because in all of the dispersions of codfish skin collagen we have prepared, we found a few large thermostable fibrils that retained their identity indefinitely.

In general, variability seems to be the rule rather than the exception. Swollen fibrils derived from the serous layer of beef small intestine, for example, are very small and approximately of the same diameter (Fig. 13). It is quite obvious that they are very different in appearance from the leg tendon fibrils of the same species shown in Fig. 4. To go to an opposite extreme, the fibrils in kangaroo tail tendon are not only very much larger but show a wide range of fibril diameters (Fig. 14). These fibrils are by far the largest that we have examined to date, with the possible exception of swollen fibrils in very old dispersions of beef leg tendon collagen. Of course, one may question whether the larger fibrils really consist of two or more smaller fibrils that cannot be resolved in the optical microscope. If this were the case, we would expect to see the ends of the larger fibrils broomed out occasionally, particularly since the dispersions are usually made up in a Waring blendor. We have examined thousands of fibril ends in the phase-contrast microscope and have yet to see one that is broomed out. In the electron microscope, the large swollen fibrils show no sign of being bundles of smaller fibrils, as can be seen in the fortuitous arrangement of beef leg tendon fibrils shown in Fig. 15. The swollen fibrils usually end abruptly without any sign of subdivision into smaller longitudinal elements (Fig 16), so I think we can say with confidence that variations in the diameters of the fibrils is not due to an aggregation of smaller fibrils.

In using the acid swelling technique, we had hoped that we would be able to make the tropocollagen units or chains resolvable

---

Fig. 15. Electron micrograph of PTA-stained swollen collagen fibrils obtained from beef leg tendon, showing that the large fibrils are not resolvable into bundles of smaller fibrils. This is demonstrated again in the cross section of dehydrated tendon shown in Fig. 21. Magnification: 15,750 ×.

Fig. 16. Electron micrograph of PTA-stained swollen beef tendon collagen fibrils, illustrating the clean-cut, unbroomed character of the end of a fibril, providing further evidence that the fibrils are structural entities. Magnification: 7,290 ×.

Fig. 17. Electron micrograph of tactoidal forms reconstituted from a solution of enzyme-depolymerized "insoluble" collagen. Magnification: 15,750 ×.

Fig. 18. Electron micrograph of SLS forms reconstituted from a solution of enzyme-depolymerized "insoluble" collagen. Magnification: 126,000 ×.

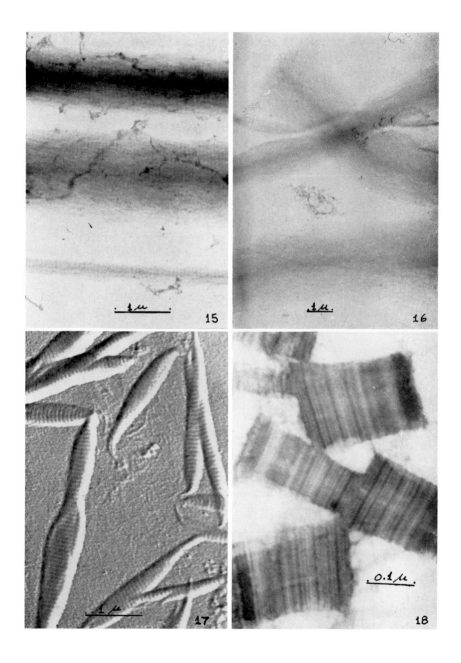

by spreading them out. We failed in this, so we decided to try to take the fibril apart by another method. Dr. Irving Oneson of our staff had discovered that the swollen "insoluble" fibrils could be depolymerized to a soluble form by several proteolytic enzymes, such as pepsin and ficin. Furthermore, he found that he could reconstitute fibrils, tactoids, and SLS forms with typical collagen periodicity from this soluble material, using methods developed by the Massachusetts Institute of Technology group (Figs. 17, 18). The recovery was very high, approaching about 80% of the original collagen. We interpreted this to mean that the enzyme digestion splits out the tropo units by breaking the lateral and end-to-end linkages without affecting the units per se. These results suggested that, by following the enzyme digestion process with a time series of observations in both the optical and electron microscopes, we might be able to visualize the breakup of the swollen fibrils and thus learn something about how they are put together. Optically, the course of the digestion of the fibrils was characterized by a loss of contrast of the fibrils and an apparent increase in their average diameter. This was followed by a decrease in the number of fibrils. Figure 19 shows swollen fibrils after several hours of digestion with ficin. Though the contrast is very much lower than in the control (Fig. 4), the dense central cores are distinctly visible, providing further evidence for the intrafibrillar differentiation mentioned previously. In support of the direct optical observations, Dr. Oneson determined that the initial stages of digestion are accompanied by a rapid increase in the viscosity of the dispersion as the fibrils swell (Text Fig. 3). This is followed by a gradual decline in the viscosity as the fibril population decreases.

We were frankly disappointed when we examined the enzyme-digested swollen fibrils in the electron microscope (Fig. 20). We

---

FIG. 19.   Phase-contrast photomicrograph of swollen beef leg tendon fibrils after several hours of treatment with ficin. Magnification: 1,170 ×.

FIG. 20.   Electron micrograph of a swollen beef leg tendon fibril after several hours of treatment with ficin. The limits of the fibril are shown between the arrows. Magnification: 8,190 ×.

FIG. 21.   Electron micrograph of a cross section of methacrylate-embedded beef leg tendon showing the solid, round cross-sectional configuration of the collagen fibrils in the completely dehydrated state. The space between the fibrils is a dehydration artifact. Magnification: 64,800 ×.

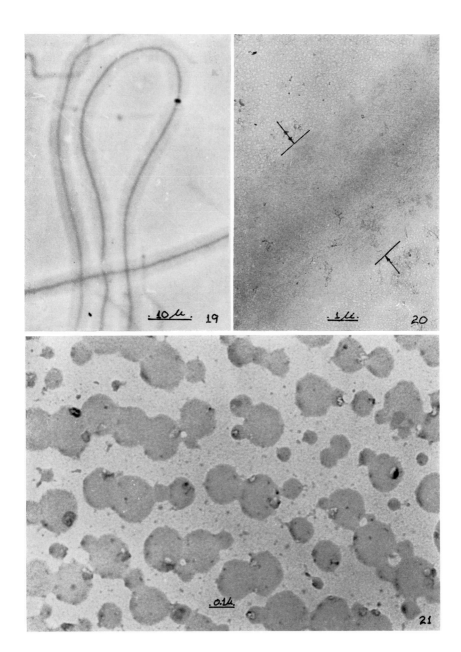

were unable to visualize the splitting out of the tropocollagen units, even though many of the fibrils were so thin and transparent that they could scarcely be distinguished from the supporting film. Shortly after the beginning of the digestion process, all fibrils lost their periodic structure, probably because of their highly swollen state, and we could find no evidence for any kind of orientation in the fibril substance.

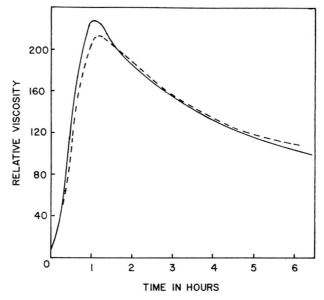

Text Fig. 3. Changes in viscosity of a dispersion of swollen collagen fibrils after the addition of a solution of ficin.

The use of thin-sectioning techniques has given us some rather important information, but has not proven to be a very satisfactory way of getting at the fundamental structure of the fibrils. Cross sections of methacrylate-embedded beef leg tendon (Fig. 21) rule out the possibility that the fibrils are hollow—but this has already been ruled out by the discovery of the dense central region in the swollen fibrils. The diameters of the fibrils in beef leg tendon do not form a continuous spectrum but fall into three classes averaging about 500, 1,000, and 2,000 Å. This information argues against the idea that the fibrils grow by the continuous accretion of tropocollagen units on their surface, since this would require a continuous spectrum of fibril diameters. A longitudinal section of unswollen collagen fibrils (Fig. 22) confirms the solid condition of the fibril, and also tells us that the electron-dense cross bands extend through the entire diameter of the fibril. We have not seen a dense central region in any of our thin sections of unswollen fibrils. This seems to become visible only as a result of a difference in swellability in acid media. As with the acid-swollen and enzyme-digested fibrils,

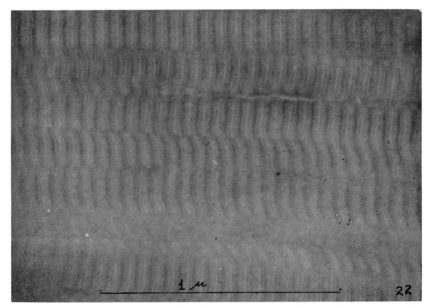

FIG. 22. Electron micrograph of a chrome-stained longitudinal section of beef leg tendon collagen fibrils, showing the continuity of the electron-dense cross bands through the entire diameter of the fibrils. Magnification: 64,800 ×.

we were unable to visualize the fundamental organization of the tropocollagen units in our conventionally sectioned material.

In our constant search for new ways of visualizing the fine structure of the collagen fibril, we have stumbled on some rather odd techniques. The latest involves the use of thin sections of unfixed and unembedded collagenous tissues. Animal tendons or hides dried at room temperature form translucent, hard, self-supporting masses that can be sectioned for both optical and electron microscopy without any further treatment. The collagen fibrils are not altered chemically by this simple procedure, so that the sections can be digested with enzymes, swollen in acid media, or handled in any manner that the ingenuity of the investigator can devise. Figures 1 and 2 are optical photomicrographs of 5-micron sections of tendon and hide that were prepared by this method. Figure 23 shows an electron micrograph of a thin section of cowhide prepared in a similar manner. We made the mistake of cutting the first set of thin sections at about 250 Å. At this thickness, the col-

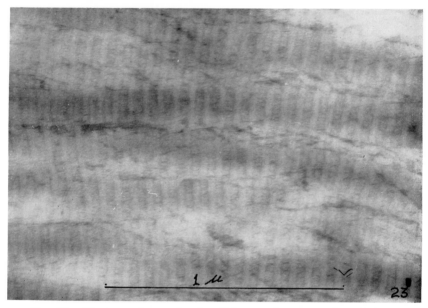

Fig. 23. Electron micrograph of a PTA-stained section of cowhide prepared without fixing or embedding the tissue. Magnification: 64,800 ×.

lagen was almost completely transparent in the electron beam, probably because of water pickup in the sectioning trough. In the wet condition, the fibrils were swollen to perhaps two or three times their completely dehydrated volume and appeared to be considerably larger than the fibrils found in conventionally prepared thin sections where swelling is prevented by fixation and embedment in methacrylate. Increasing contrast by staining with PTA or other electron stains proved fruitless until the sections were cut at 750–1,000 Å. In sections prepared by this technique we began to see some suggestion of internal structure in the fibrils, oriented in the manner predicted by theory. In addition, there is an electron-dense component between the hide collagen fibrils. It is possible that this component may be a cement substance that holds the fibrils together.

Though we have not, as yet, been able to visualize the tropocollagen units directly, we have learned a good deal about the grosser aspects of the "insoluble" fibrils. We were particularly impressed by the value of using combined optical and electron microscopic observations—it was through these methods that we established the presence of a dense central region in the fibrils and the 2-dimensional nature of the swelling reaction in beef leg tendon fibrils. We are just beginning to exploit enzyme digestion and thin sectioning of unaltered collagen and hope that, by combining these techniques, we will be able to proceed a little further into the fundamental structure of the collagen fibril.

The Keratins

HAROLD P. LUNDGREN AND WILFRED H. WARD

Western Utilization Research and Development Division, Agricultural Research Service, United States Department of Agriculture, Albany, California

INTRODUCTION

This review describes and illustrates the main features of keratin structure. Information contributed by electron microscopists is given special notice. Evidence from optical microscopy and, especially, from x-ray diffraction is interpreted, with a measure of speculation, to give a basis for understanding trends in keratin research most closely relaetd to electron microscopy. Pertinent chemical evidence is considered. However, this is so rudimentary that a detailed description of chemical structure is not possible. In the interest of appropriate brevity, much important evidence from chemical reactivity, mechanical properties, and spectroscopy is not mentioned.

KERATINS IN GENERAL

Definition, Natural Occurrence

Keratins are natural, cellular systems of fibrous proteins cross-linked by cystine sulfur. They have evolved primarily as a barrier to the environment, serving to protect the higher vertebrates—amphibians, reptiles, birds, and mammals—from the stresses of life. Keratins occur as the principal constituents of the horny outermost layer of the epidermis and of related appendages, such as horns, hooves, scales, hair, and feathers, that are derived from the skin. Table I summarizes their natural occurrence. It lists also some secreted fibrous proteins that may be usefully distinguished from keratins because of differences in structure and composition.

Characteristic keratin properties are given in Table II. In general,

39

TABLE I
Keratinized Structures

	Skin	Callus	Scales	Claws Nails	Hooves	Horn	Hair Fur Wool	Feather	Other
Fishes:	(No keratinized structures, with possible exception of horny warts or "teeth" of some species)								
Amphibians:	α	—	Absent	(Horny claws or "teeth" of some species not characterized)					
Reptiles:	β, α	β, α	β, α	β, α	Absent	—	Absent	Absent	Beak, outer shell of turtle
Birds:	α, or β with components		Legs, β	α	Absent	—	Absent	Hard, mainly β	Beak, β and α
Mammals:	Soft, α	Soft, α	Hard, α (Rat tail armadillo pangolin)	Hard, α	Hard, α	Hard, α	Hard, α	Absent	Whale baleen, α

Secreted, Non-keratin Structures

Skeleton of "keratinous" sponges
Byssus threads of molluscs
Silk fibroin, resilin
Scales of fishes
Egg cases of molluscs, insects, fishes, reptiles
Egg shell membranes of birds

"Neurokeratin"
Collagen, elastin

keratins are tough, elastic, and insoluble, and are elaborated into structures adapted for mechanical protection, warmth, abrasion resistance, and special purposes such as grasping, tearing, feeling, digging, climbing, fighting, eating, flight, and ornamentation. Keratin structures may be pliable, as required for body movement,

TABLE II
SUMMARY OF KERATIN PROPERTIES

Biological origin:	Higher vertebrates; organized, consolidated, dead cell residues
Physical properties:	Tough, horny, elastic, insoluble in dilute aqueous media
Composition:	Protein, heterogeneous; high and low sulfur components; low or moderate in proline; fairly high average residue weight (*116*). "Soft" keratins relatively low in sulfur
Structure:	Hydrogen-bonded within (α) or among (β) individual polypeptide chains. α Component typically forms helical strand with some crystallinity, dimensions characteristic also of muscle, fibrin, and unconsolidated epidermal tissue. Feather type differs in having crystalline β component predominant

or they may achieve sufficient rigidity for other purposes by consolidation in mass, sometimes on a bony core. Thus, keratins are fascinating for the great variety of structures and purposes to which they have become adapted.

Levels of Organization: Methods for Determining Structure

From a chemist's viewpoint, the goal of structural research is to define the nature, spatial arrangement, and interconnections of the atoms making up the material under study. But the difference in scale between atomic distances and the size of an object that we can see—even so small an object as a wool fiber—is so great that for comprehension we are forced to consider structure in successive levels of organization. This is especially true for complex materials such as keratins. The problem is clearly shown in Table III, which gives, in rough figures, dimensions of successively smaller structural features of a wool fiber.

In considering dimensions of structural organization, it may be of interest to note that a typical fine wool fiber, growing about 2 inches in a year, then grows about 16 Å per second on the average. Taking the diameter of such a fiber as 20 microns, growth amounts to 5×10^{11} Å^3 per second. The sheep takes 13 seconds to make a length of fine wool equal to one x-ray repeat distance, 200 Å. The wool follicle makes 20 million keratin units (assumed average molecular weight 20,000) per second.

TABLE III

REPRESENTATIVE WOOL FIBER DIMENSIONS

200,000	Å —	Diameter of wool fiber
20,000	Å —	Diameter of wool cortical cell
2,000	Å —	Diameter of macrofibril
200	Å —	Thickness of cell membrane
80	Å —	Diameter of microfibril
20	Å —	Diameter of protofibril
11	Å —	Diameter of α-helix
1.5	Å —	Atomic spacing

Three physical instruments have been of key importance in determining structure at these various levels: the optical microscope, the electron microscope, and the x-ray diffraction camera. The electron microscope is especially important because it covers the critical gap between the smallest detail that can be seen with the light microscope and the largest periodicities observable by x-ray diffraction. Electron microscopy is also important because it is so new that its techniques are still being rapidly improved and its application to keratins still being vigorously developed.

Optical microscopy is used for studying detail down to about 0.5 micron. It is invaluable for showing details of growth and structure at the level of biological tissues and cells down to the larger cell components. With its help, the organization and development of keratinizing tissues, form, and chemical reactivity, have been extensively explored, providing the necessary framework of reference for methods of greater resolving power. It has established the cellular nature of keratins. In the case of wool, cited again for purposes of illustration, optical microscopy (Fig. 1) shows the surface scales, about 15 microns long on the average (1), and, with some difficulty, the relief of the scale edges, 1 micron or less. For comparison, Fig. 2 shows a replica of a wool fiber surface as observed by electron microscopy (2). Again, with reference to Table III, optical microscopy shows that the cortical cell residues, about 2 microns in diameter, have a fibrous, oriented substructure;

FIG. 1. Imprint of 20-micron wool fiber in gelatin (photographed with the optical microscope by Dr. F. T. Jones). Surface detail is more easily seen than with the original fiber because of absence of scattered light from the back side of the fiber. Magnification: 400 ×.

but details of the larger fibrous units, the macrofibrils, roughly 0.2 micron in diameter, are beyond the limit of resolution (Fig. 3).

At the other extreme, x-ray diffraction, with the help of chemical information, provides evidence of how the polypeptide chains (Fig. 4), of which the keratin proteins consist, are arranged in the more ordered parts of the structure. From this evidence we know that the chains exist in two fundamental ordered forms, one helical and one relatively extended. In many cases, x-ray diffraction gives additional evidence that is less easily interpreted. In any case, further information is needed to show how the ordered and less ordered regions are arranged in the larger framework.

Thanks to electron microscopy, important progress is being made in determining details between the levels of peptide chain arrangement and cellular structure. For example, electron microscopy has shown that keratins of widely different character are composed of fibrillar units, 60–80 Å in diameter (microfibrils, tonofibrils) aggregated in characteristic ways (4–6). Even finer detail is on the verge of resolution. With the help of x-ray diffraction, such detail may be elucidated even though it does not readily yield to either technique by itself (7–9).

Electron microscopy also supplements the optical microscope by showing details of morphogenesis not accessible to the latter. In this way it furthers understanding of protein synthesis in general. The electron microscope reveals in epidermis (6) and hair follicles (4, 5) not only the initial appearance of the fibrous units, but also successive stages of their aggregation, organization, and hardening. Such studies provide means of observing effects of genetic differences, nutrition, and disease on structural details that are not accessible by other means.

Classification of Keratins

Various aspects of properties, function, and structure have been used to classify keratins. One classification distinguishes *soft* keratin, such as skin keratin, from *hard* keratin, such as horn, on the basis of sulfur content. Thus, keratins with a sulfur content of 3% or more, such as horn, hoof, feather, and hair have been described

---

Fig. 2. Polystyrene negative replica of 21-micron wool fiber, chromium-shadowed, as recorded by electron microscopy [from Swerdlow and Seeman (2)].

10 μ

45

FIG. 3. Cortical cell residues about 80 microns long released from mohair by acid digestion (photographed between crossed Polaroid films with the optical microscope by Dr. F. T. Jones). The birefringence is due to the substructure of oriented fibrils not resolved by the optical microscope. Magnification: 600 ×.

as hard. The higher sulfur contents result from incorporation of sulfur-rich components during keratinization. As we shall see, some —and very likely all—of these include characteristic components that are low in sulfur.

Another keratin classification depends on differences in the fine structure shown by x-ray diffraction. The main ordered fibrous component of mammalian keratin consists predominantly of polypeptide chains in the helical configuration, whereas a more extended form is characteristic of many keratin structures of reptiles and birds (10).

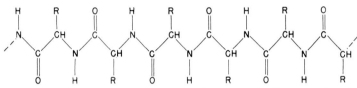

Fig. 4. Diagram showing the order of connection, but not the spatial relationship, of atoms in a polypeptide (protein). R indicates a side chain, any of about 20 different groups of atoms, which influence the conformation of the protein and its interaction with other units.

Thirty years ago Astbury (11), whose x-ray diffraction studies have been a continuing stimulus and guide to the study of keratin structure, recognized the existence of two types of configuration in proteins. He deduced that the polypeptide chains in mammalian hairs occur in a "folded" configuration, which he designated the α-keratin structure, clearly distinguishing it from the more extended, β-keratin configuration, similar to that found by Brill (12) and Meyer and Mark (13) in silk fibroin (not a keratin) as a limiting case, into which α-keratin can be reversibly transformed when stretched. Although the folded structure proposed by Astbury differs in detail from the presently accepted helical form, the underlying inference is maintained. In the α form, the spacing of the amino acid residues in the axial direction is very close to one-half of the axial spacing observed in the β form.

Astbury and his colleagues later showed that the α structure is common to several fibrous proteins, including muscle, epidermin, fibrinogen, and fibrin, which he therefore classed together with keratin as the KMEF group (14). He also called attention to the natural occurrence of keratin in feathers and reptilian claws and scales in the β form, although not so fully extended as in stretched hair or silk. Astbury's classification (*14–16*) is summarized in Table IV, which indicates the relationship of keratins to other fibrous proteins.

TABLE IV

ASTBURY'S CLASSIFICATION OF FIBROUS PROTEINS

I.   KMEF Group

α Subgroup
1. Fibrous proteins of the epidermis of mammals, amphibians, and certain fishes (epidermins and keratins)
2. Fibrous structures such as hair, horn, nails that arise from the mammalian epidermis (keratins)
3. Myosin
4. Fibrinogen and fibrin

In α-keratin, the polypeptide chains are regularly "folded" into a form about half as long as the fully extended length. They can be extended, often reversibly, into an almost fully extended β form and supercontracted into a still shorter form.

β Subgroup
1. Silk fibroin (most fully extended configuration)
2. β Phases produced from the α subgroup by stress
3. Feather, beaks, claws, tortoise shell, scales, derived from the epidermis of birds and reptiles (characteristic of principal, keratin components)
4. F-Actin

II. Collagen Group

III. Miscellaneous
1. Elastin
2. Reticulin

Keratins may also be classified on the basis of differences in function. Although the various keratin structures are specialized developments of the epidermis, they have characteristic differences adapting them for specific uses. The "soft" skin keratin with low sulfur content and poor fibrillar orientation may be viewed as an adaptation for pliability and changes in contour. At the other extreme, the well-ordered β components of flight feathers, flexible but with limited extensibility, are well suited to light-weight, cantilevered, stress-bearing structures.

The Chemical Nature of Keratins

At this point we review some of the chemical properties of keratins that are most closely related to their structure. Although keratins are formed naturally in association with other materials, principally lipids, which may influence their development, the insoluble proteins are considered the characteristic constituents. Other substances can be removed by careful cleaning and solvent extraction to a level of the order of 0.2%.

As proteins, keratins yield amino acids on hydrolysis. Their over-all composition may be specified in terms of the various amino

TABLE V

Amino Acid Composition of Selected Keratins

(In grams of constituent from 100 gm keratin)

Amino acid	Human skin[a]	Merino wool[b]	Porcupine quill tip[c]	Turkey feather[d]
Alanine	6.9	3.70	4.62	7.66
Arginine	4.3	10.24	9.97	6.18
Aspartic acid	4.7	7.03	8.58	7.41
Cystine	9.1	10.27	9.92	8.48
Glutamic acid	13.2	14.92	17.05	8.84
Glycine	3.7	5.51	6.14	10.14
Histidine	2.9	0.90	0.83	0.34
Isoleucine	2.1	3.19	3.74	3.90
Leucine	10.2	7.99	9.23	9.37
Lysine	7.9	2.79	3.64	0.88
Methionine	2.0	0.60	—	0.39
Phenylalanine	7.1	3.95	4.22	5.75
Proline	6.6	7.12	5.74	10.97
Serine	8.3	9.89	8.35	14.09
Threonine	6.0	6.15	5.23	4.51
Tryptophan	2.5	1.89	—	—
Tyrosine	3.7	6.50	6.76	2.91
Valine	6.7	4.94	5.86	8.65

[a] Total palmar *stratum corneum*, from Müting *et al.* (*17*).
[b] Average of data for 64's and 70's quality, from Simmonds (*18*).
[c] From North American porcupine, *Erethizon* sp., from Fraser *et al.* (*19*).
[d] Rachis from white feathers, from Schroeder *et al.* (*20*).

acids. Results for selected keratins are compiled in Table V. However, from their mode of formation and microscopic diversity it is evident that keratins are mixtures. These compositions are therefore averages for the different components. Separation of the components has been only partly successful, as will be discussed presently.

In proteins, the residues of the amino acids (with removal of the elements of water) are linked into chains as already diagrammed in Fig. 4. To determine structure on the chemical level, the different sorts of protein chain must be distinguished and the order of the amino acid residues in each sort must be determined. Such studies have not been completed for any keratin. Nevertheless it is pertinent to mention a few basic chemical properties.

Keratins as a group are relatively insoluble in reagents which dissolve other proteins without destroying them. Associated with insolubility are characteristic limitation of swelling in polar liquids and relative resistance to hydrolysis. These properties are largely due to cystine residues, which provide disulfide cross links holding

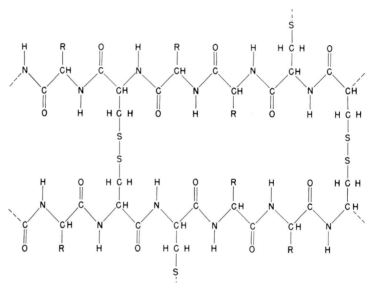

FIG. 5. Diagram showing the cross-linking of polypeptide chains by the disulfide bridges of cystine residues.

the polypeptide chains together in mass as diagrammed in Fig. 5. On the other hand, degradation of keratins in certain environments results from chemical reactivity of the disulfide cross links. These cross links can be broken by various chemical reactions including:

(a) reduction:
$$RSSR + 2 \, [H] \longrightarrow 2RSH$$
(b) oxidation:
$$RSSR + 6 \, [O] + 2e \longrightarrow 2 \, RSO_3$$
(c) hydrolysis:
$$RSSR + HOH \longrightarrow RSH + RSOH$$
(d) disulfide exchange especially in alkaline or strongly acid environments:
$$RSSR + R'SH \longrightarrow RSSR' + RSH$$

The ease with which disulfide cross links in keratins undergo such reactions depends on the local structure. Some of the cross links are considerably less stable than others, presumably because the immediately surrounding structure is more "open," or in other words, either less sterically inhibited, less hydrogen-bonded, or amorphous rather than crystalline. A more open structure provides easier access of reagents that cleave the disulfide cross links.

Recent successes of electron microscopy in distinguishing details of natural keratin structures depend in part on improvements in methods for making thin sections of these tough materials (21, 22) and in part on differential staining with heavy metals (8, 9, 22, 23). Fully hardened keratin contains very few sulfhydryl groups, but these can be greatly increased by hydrolysis or, especially, reduction. Differential staining of reduced keratin by certain metals, notably osmium and lead, has been particularly successful in disclosing fine structure. When dense staining by such metals is observed in electron micrographs, such staining is commonly taken to indicate regions of high sulfur content. However, it should also be borne in mind that differential staining can also result from differences in accessibility. That is, differences in distribution may be modified or confused by differences in accessibility. Such considerations hold also for other reactive groups in proteins: tyrosine residues, or carboxyl or basic groups, which also show differential reactivity toward more or less specific reagents such as metal ions, dyes, deuterium, and iodine. The influence of local accessibility remains to be defined by comparing preparations stained with reagents of varied molecular size.

The sulfur or cystine contents of keratins vary widely, as shown in Table VI. The keratinized layer of skin, which may be taken as the prototype of keratin, is among those with the least sulfur. Other keratins are formed by specially adapted modifications of epidermis. A common feature of these modifications is that a localized region of primary growth is especially well supplied with blood vessels. Keratin forms in cells displaced away from the region of primary growth. Provision is made for incorporation of sulfur-rich components into the structure as it hardens. The differences in sulfur content of the various keratins very likely result in part from differences in the proportion of components high and low in sulfur. Experimental support for this view rests on separation of keratin fractions differing in sulfur content, examples of which (in the case of wool) are compiled in Table VII. A variety of evidence, discussed for example by Rogers (*34*), identifies a low sulfur fraction with fibrils observable by electron microscopy, embedded in a non-fibrous matrix with higher sulfur content. Corresponding protein fractions have been isolated from wool roots or prepared

TABLE VI

SULFUR CONTENTS OF VARIOUS KERATINS

Source	S (%)
Turkey feather rachis	2.6
African porcupine, de-scaled quill tip	2.7
Human skin, palmar *stratum corneum*	2.9
Mohair, Turkey	3.0
Camel hair	3.3
Goat, Tunisian, hair	3.5
Wool, Merino	3.7
Human hair	3.9
Alpaca hair	3.9
Dog hair	5.1
Rabbit hair	5.2

TABLE VII

SULFUR CONTENTS OF WOOL FIBER FRACTIONS[a]

Method of Extraction	Fractions obtained		References
	Low S (% S)	High S (% S)	
Hydrochloric acid	1.4	4.1	Trotman *et al.* (*25*)
Alkaline thioglycolate	3.3	4.5	Goddard and Michaelis (*26*)
Cetyl sulfonic acid	4.2	7.5	Lindley (*27*)
Peracetic acid, ammonia	2.4	6.1	Alexander and Earland (*28*)
Chlorine dioxide	1.3	5.3	Speakman and Das (*29*)
Alkaline thioglycolate	1.5	6.5	Gillespie and Lennox (*30*); Gillespie (*31*)
Hydrochloric acid	3.53	7.35	Ward and Bartulovich (*32*)
Peracetic acid, ammonia	1.9	5.8	Corfield *et al.* (*33*)
Urea extract of "wool roots"	1.7	4.1	Rogers (*34*)
Performic acid, pH 8 extraction	1.96	4.72	O'Donnell and Thompson (*35*) and unpublished data
Hydrochloric acid, reduction, acrylonitrile	1.7	—	Bartulovich *et al.* (*36*)

[a] Modified from Gillespie (*24*).

TABLE VIII

AMINO ACID COMPOSITION OF WOOL FRACTIONS[a]

a: Grams constituent from 100 gm protein

b: Millimoles constituent from 100 gm protein

Amino acid	α-Keratose		γ-Keratose		S-Carboxymethylkerateines				Wool root protein	
					Low sulfur		High sulfur			
	a	b	a	b	a	b	a	b	a	b
Alanine	4.92	55.2	2.22	24.9	5.24	58.8	2.25	25.2	4.42	49.6
Arginine	10.35	59.4	7.98	45.8	11.86	68.1	8.87	50.9	8.61	49.4
Aspartic acid	9.49	71.3	2.30	17.3	10.78	81.0	3.39	25.5	8.82	66.3
Cystine	5.11	42.5	16.79	139.8	5.36	44.6	19.27	160.4	3.87	32.2
Glutamic acid	18.33	124.6	8.31	56.5	18.36	124.8	10.65	72.4	13.80	93.8
Glycine	4.42	58.9	3.59	47.8	4.52	60.2	4.43	59.0	4.03	53.7
Histidine	0.74	4.8	0.79	5.1	1.01	6.5	1.06	6.8	3.74	24.1
Isoleucine	3.73	28.4	2.73	20.7	4.34	33.1	4.01	30.6	3.84	29.3
Leucine	10.93	83.3	3.23	24.6	11.37	86.7	4.35	33.2	9.48	72.3
Lysine	3.84	26.3	0.73	5.0	5.20	35.6	0.77	5.3	5.19	35.5
Phenylalanine	3.67	22.2	1.83	11.1	4.11	24.9	2.66	16.1	3.35	20.3
Proline	3.53	30.7	10.93	94.9	3.53	30.7	14.08	122.3	3.17	27.5
Serine	8.04	76.5	9.83	93.5	7.60	72.3	13.46	128.1	5.69	54.1
Threonine	4.69	39.4	8.55	71.8	4.96	41.6	11.95	100.3	4.11	34.5
Tyrosine	5.06	27.9	2.46	13.6	5.69	31.4	3.32	18.3	4.35	24.0
Valine	5.32	45.4	4.69	40.0	5.72	48.8	5.67	48.4	4.47	38.2

[a] From data compiled by Crewther and Dowling (37) from analyses by Corfield et al. (33), Gillespie and associates (38), and Rogers (39).

Cystine derivatives are recorded as cystine, counting one "mole" per sulfur atom.

from wool after breaking cross links by oxidation or reduction. Unequivocally pure fractions have not been demonstrated. However, amino acid analyses show certain regularities. These are directly pertinent to the determination of structure, so that representative examples are cited in Table VIII. Some of the significant features will be discussed later.

PARTICULAR KERATINS

Skin Keratin

Since keratins form as modifications of the epidermis, we now summarize the formation of skin keratin as a basis for understanding the development of more specialized structures that are in many ways more clearly defined. The skin of vertebrates is a layered structure of muscle, fat, connective tissue (with ample blood supply), and on the outer surface, an epidermis which produces keratin as its outermost layer, as well as in specially derived structures such as hair. The microscopic anatomy of skin, especially mammalian or human skin, has been reviewed by Montagna (40).

In the higher vertebrates, the epidermis consists of an external keratinized layer of coherent, flattened dead cell residues and an inner layer showing a systematic transition from a proliferating basal layer to the dead, keratinized surface. The living underlayer of the epidermis is designated the *stratum Malpighii* or *mucosum* and may be further subclassified into the *stratum basale* or *germinativum*, and, progressing toward the surface, the *stratum spinosum* (with a further subdivision, the *stratum granulosum*) and, in the thick skin of palms and soles, a conspicuous *stratum lucidum*. The fully keratinized layer is designated the *stratum corneum*. Figure 6 shows these relationships.

These epidermal layers vary in thickness and in detail with the site and with the animal species. The skin of fishes, for example, is essentially unkeratinized. Nevertheless protein isolated from fish epidermis shows an α x-ray diffraction pattern and therefore structural detail similar to that of protein from the epidermis of higher vertebrates (10). A significant feature of keratinization is that cell division occurs in such a way that some cells are progressively displaced away from their supply of metabolites. They undergo regular degenerative changes resulting in loss of water, nucleic acid, carbohydrates, and certain other constituents, and in accumulation of proteins that made up the keratin proper, "contaminated," however, with "nuclear remnants and cytoplasmic debris." As the layers are displaced, the outermost may be worn off or cast off in flakes or layers.

Microscopic and electron microscopic studies have shown that all parts of the growing layer contain protein filaments (Fig. 7), tonofilaments or tonofibrils, with diameters of about 50 Å, dispersed in the cell cytoplasm. These filaments are oriented roughly perpendicular to the cell surfaces, become densely aggregated in the

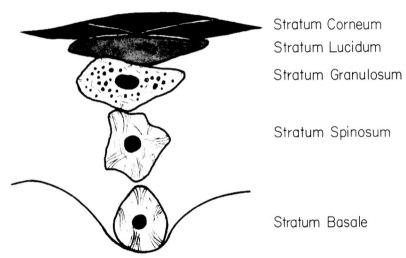

Stratum Corneum

Stratum Lucidum

Stratum Granulosum

Stratum Spinosum

Stratum Basale

FIG. 6. Diagram illustrating the forms and progressive changes of cells in the various layers of the epidermis [from Matoltsy (41)].

stratum spinosum, and stain in a way suggesting periodic variation in composition or structure. In the *stratum granulosum* numerous keratohyalin granules, 100 Å in diameter or larger, appear in association with the filaments. These granules stain readily with basic or acid dyes. They are reported (40) to be relatively heavily mineralized, containing calcium, as well as protein, lipid, and acid mucopolysaccharide. They lack thiol and disulfide groups although the cytoplasm of the *stratum granulosum* has a substantial thiol content. They have a film or capsule of ribonucleoprotein.

Truly keratinized filaments form in the *stratum granulosum*. In human skin (6) after keratinization the filaments have a diameter of about 74 Å, which is larger than that of the primary tonofila-

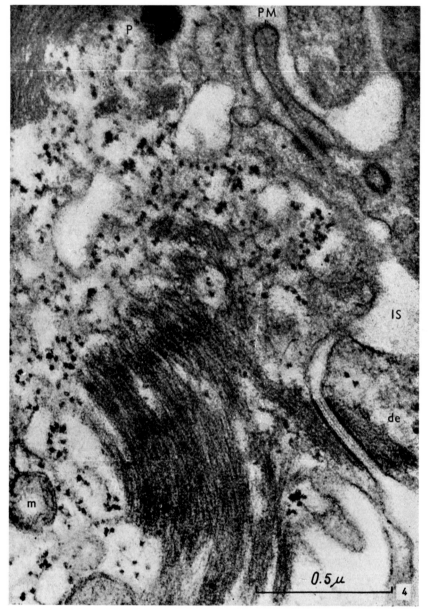

Fig. 7. Tonofilaments, the smallest keratin-forming fibrils, shown in the basal layer of human skin by electron microscopy [from Brody (6)]. The individual tonofilaments are grouped in bundles of varying size. The fibrous part of a desmosome (de) between adjoining cells is shown to be closely related to the tono-

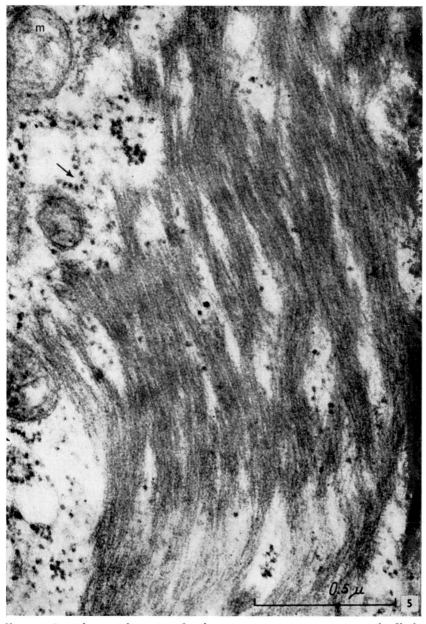

filaments. Irregular particles, not uniformly opaque, occur in spaces among the fibrils, sometimes in short chains (arrow); IS denotes intercellular space; m, mitochondria; P, pigment; PM, plasma membrane.

ments. They are normally aggregated in bundles to make keratin-ized fibrils about 250 Å in diameter. The bundles include about 5–10 filaments, with a space of about 30 Å between individual fila-ments and a somewhat larger space between the bundles. The keratinized fibrils are oriented approximately parallel to the skin surface, but are not aligned with one another, so that they scatter x-rays independently (42). The degree of order or orientation is scarcely sufficient to permit clear inferences of finer structural detail from x-ray diffraction, but variations in abnormal keratiniza-tion have been interpreted in terms of fibrillar diameter (43).

The role of keratohyalin is not known. It has been suggested that the tonofilaments may be incorporated into the keratohyalin granules and that the latter are the immediate keratin precursors; or they may supply cementing or matrix material, perhaps taking part in incorporating sulfur from the cytoplasm.

The keratinized (human) epidermal layer finally consists of about 65% insoluble protein with about 2% sulfur. Typical "hard" kera-tins such as hair contain substantially more sulfur. Other constitu-ents include about 10% of soluble protein, 10% of low molecular weight substances including amino acids and nuclear remnants, 5% of cell membranes, and about 7–9% lipid. The fact that both soluble epidermal proteins and keratinized epidermis show the typical α pattern (Fig. 8), with characteristic spacings of about 5 Å in the (meridional) direction of preferred fibril orientation and about 9.8 Å in the perpendicular (equatorial) direction, is now interpreted as evidence that all of these materials contain ordered components with a specific helical configuration of the polypeptide chains with extensive hydrogen bonding between units in the same chain. The helices are of the order of 11 Å in effective diameter, so that a group of about 30–60, with associated, perhaps non-protein, material would be required to make up a tonofilament.

The epidermis and epidermal appendages of reptiles show a significant further development. For example, the scales and epi-dermis of snakes have two distinct cornified layers, a loose, soft, opaque, inner layer showing a typical α x-ray diffraction pattern and an outer, compact, transparent layer. The latter shows a distinct β x-ray diffraction pattern, similar in essential detail to that of stretched wool (Fig. 9), characterized by meridional spacings (in the direction of protein chain alignment) of about 3.3, 7, and 25 Å and equatorial spacings of about 4.7 and 9.7 Å. This is closely

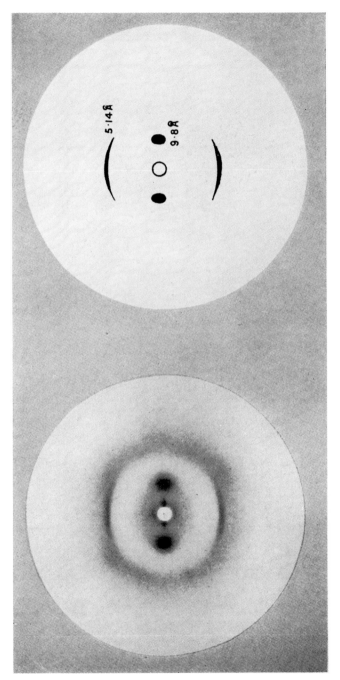

FIG. 8. The x-ray diffraction pattern of a Lincoln wool fiber, showing features characteristic of α structure [from Wool Science Review (44)]. The fiber axis is vertical and perpendicular to the x-ray beam. A different, tilted, orientation is necessary to reveal the 1.5-Å spacing characteristic of the α-helix.

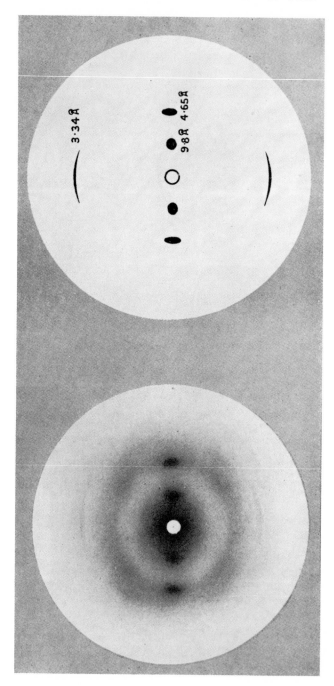

Fig. 9. The x-ray diffraction pattern of Lincoln wool stretched 70%, showing features characteristic of β structure [from Wool Science Review (44)]. In this case the change from the α to the β structure can be reversed by letting the fiber relax in water.

similar to the patterns given by feather, and as a limiting case, silk fibroin. Keratins having the α configuration can be transformed into the β state by wet heat and stretching. The x-ray and related evidence indicates that the polypeptide chains in the β state are nearly, but not quite, completely extended, with extensive hydrogen bonding between amino acid residues of adjoining chains. Other keratinized structures of reptiles such as the horny plates of turtles and claws of lizards commonly show the β pattern, although in some cases, components with α configuration are also found. The occurrence of well-ordered keratin in the β configuration in reptiles is interesting as evidence of the relationship of reptiles to birds, which produce, in feathers, still more highly elaborated β-keratin.

Of the various keratins, the structures of animal hairs and corni-fied epidermis have received most attention. Because these materi-als are poorly crystalline, showing few fine structural details in x-ray diffraction, related materials, notably porcupine quill tips (45), that give less diffuse background and many more measurable spots, are often chosen for definitive study of structure. Porcupine quill tip therefore typifies α-keratin structure with, however, an unusually high degree of ordered crystallinity. Similarly the base (calamus) of a sea gull flight feather and the claw of the reptile *Varanus niloticus* may be cited as examples of keratins with well-ordered and highly crystalline β structure (10).

Careful study of a given keratin material often produces evidence of both α and β components, although one component will usually predominate and be more crystalline. The possibility of transform-ing one form into the other during manipulation must also be remembered.

Mammalian Hair Keratin

Optical Microscopy

Research on the structure of hair and wool is of special historical interest because it provided our first insight into changes of molecu-lar conformation of proteins as a result of extension (11), setting (46), and supercontraction (47). Optical microscopy studies, go-ing back to Hooke and van Leeuwenhoek, and of which we cite those of von Nathusius (48) and McMurtrie (49) in the late nine-teenth century, established the main structural features of animal hairs. This work was strengthened and extended in notable contri-butions by Hock (50), von Bergen (51), Reumuth (52–55), Auber

(56), Wildman (57), and many others (3, 40). Such studies have shown that hairs of all sorts (57–59) and wool consist of a central cortex made up of consolidated spindle-shaped cell residues covered by an adherent layer of flattened, scale-like cuticle cells, as shown in Figs. 1 and 2 and diagrammed in Figs. 10 and 11. Many

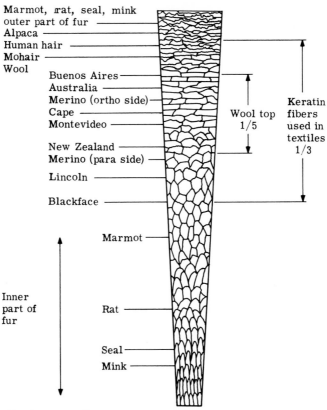

Fɪɢ. 10. Diagram illustrating the variation in scale structure and fiber diameter for various grades of wool and fur fibers from various animals [by courtesy of Professor Kassenbeck (22, 60)].

of the larger fibers, in particular, have a central medullary canal consisting of air-filled cells. Representative wool fibers have diameters ranging from 10 to 50 microns. In these, the cortex represents close to 90% of the fiber. The cortical cells range in length from 80 to 100 microns, in width from 2 to 5 microns, and in thickness from 0.5 to 1.6 microns. Estimates of the proportions of various wool fiber components are given in Table IX. The relationship of the structural components is digrammed in Fig. 12.

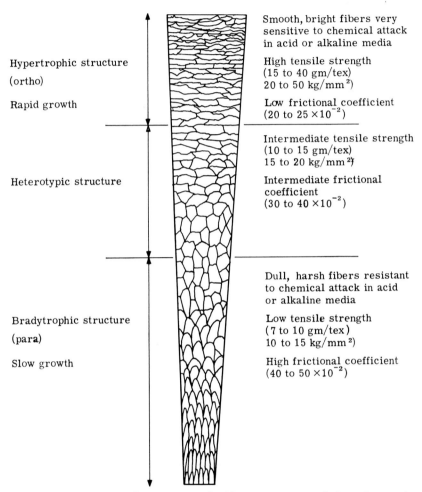

Hypertrophic structure (ortho)

Rapid growth

Heterotypic structure

Bradytrophic structure (para)

Slow growth

Smooth, bright fibers very sensitive to chemical attack in acid or alkaline media

High tensile strength (15 to 40 gm/tex) 20 to 50 kg/mm^2)

Low frictional coefficient (20 to 25 $\times 10^{-2}$)

Intermediate tensile strength (10 to 15 gm/tex) 15 to 20 kg/mm^2)

Intermediate frictional coefficient (30 to 40 $\times 10^{-2}$)

Dull, harsh fibers resistant to chemical attack in acid or alkaline media

Low tensile strength (7 to 10 gm/tex) 10 to 15 kg/mm^2)

High frictional coefficient (40 to 50 $\times 10^{-2}$)

FIG. 11. Diagram showing Kassenbeck's interpretation of the relation of scale structure, growth rate, and fiber properties [by courtesy of Professor Kassenbeck (22, 60)].

Optical microscope studies have often shown the cortex of crimped wools to have bilateral structure, shown by more or less clear-cut differences in chemical reactivity. Work of Ohara (62) calling attention to differences in dyeing may be mentioned as an example. Subsequently the meaning of these differences has been more fully appreciated and interpreted (63–70). The relation of the structural differences to crimp is shown in Fig. 13. One segment, normally found on the outside of a crimp wave, is called the *ortho* segment; its companion is called the *para* segment. Similar differences occur in the straighter wools, but the different re-

TABLE IX
Wool Fiber Components[a]

Component	%
Cuticle	20
Epicuticle	(1)
Exocuticle	
a-Layer	(1)
b-Layer	(4)
Mesocuticle	(b-layer?)
Endocuticle	(14)
Cortex	80

	Ortho segment (%)	Para segment (%)	Total (%)
Cortex			
Matrix	20	20	40
Microfibrils	10	15	25
Nuclear remnants and cell debris	5	2	7
Cell membranes			
β Layers	3	2	5
δ Layer	2	1	3

[a] Estimated percentages in fine, non-medullated wool.

gions are not arranged bilaterally. The ortho regions are more easily penetrated by most chemicals and dyes. They swell more in alkali (above about 5% sodium hydroxide). They are more readily dispersed into individual cell residues by acid or proteolytic enzymes. In untreated wool, the ortho segment is stained preferentially by basic dyes such as methylene blue; but after treatment with peracetic acid this relative affinity is reversed, very likely because the oxidized paracortex has a higher content of combined cysteic acid (derived from cystine), but possibly also because the paracortex has now been made relatively more accessible. Leveau (71) emphasizes the latter view, citing evidence that the cystine contents of the ortho and para segments are approximately the same. However, kid mohair, which has a relatively low sulfur content, has been reported to be predominantly ortho in character, while human hair, relatively high in sulfur, is predominantly para (69).

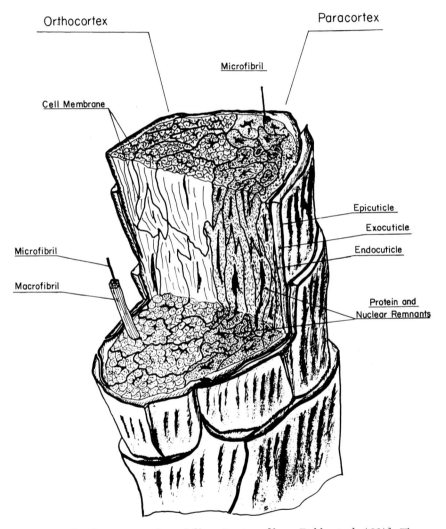

FIG. 12. Stereogram of wool fiber structure [from Dobb *et al.* (61)]. The clear-cut difference in grouping of microfibrils into macrofibrils in opposite halves of the fiber is characteristic of fine wool, diameter about 20 microns.

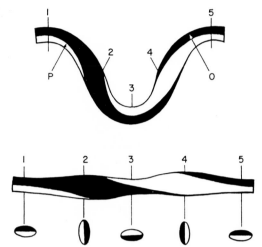

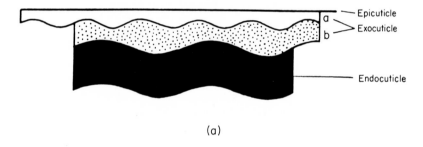

FIG. 13. Diagram showing the relationship among wool fiber crimp, ellipticity of cross section, and bilateral differentiation [from Mercer (65)].

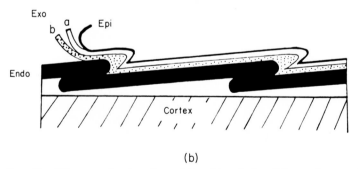

(a)

(b)

FIG. 14. Diagram showing the relationship of the different layers of the wool fiber cuticle [from Fraser and Rogers (80)]. The cuticle of other hair fibers may be many cells thick, each cell of which may be similarly layered.

The cuticle cells of animal hairs vary in size, shape, and appearance with the species, position on the animal, and other conditions of growth (57–59, 61, 72–74), as already shown in Fig. 11. Cuticle cells are of two main types: coronal, each of which completely sur-

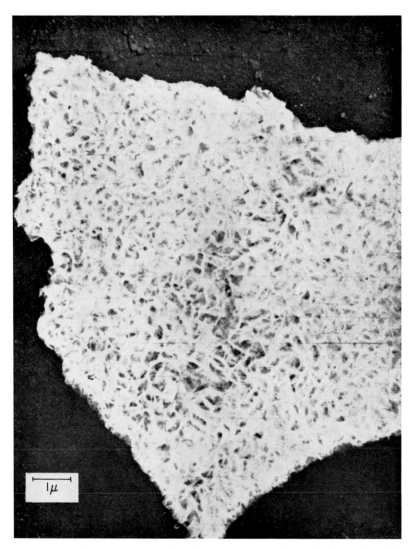

FIG. 15. Electron micrograph of the spongy residue of the endocuticle from a Cape wool fiber after trypsin digestion [from Gorter and Houwink (83)].

rounds the fiber, and imbricated, which do not. According to the animal species, coronal scales may have a continuous outer edge or one that is dentate or serrate. Imbricated scales differ similarly, and may be ovate, elongated, crenate, flattened, or acuminate.

Optical microscopy further shows that cuticle cells have two main components, distinguishable by their chemical and enzymatic reactivities. These are called the exocuticle [preferentially attacked by trypsin in the untreated fiber (75)] and endocuticle. Electron microscopy has disclosed further details of these structures both on the surface (76) and internal. In particular it confirms the presence, on the outside of the exocuticle, of an epicuticle (77–79), a chemically resistant, uniform outer membrane about 100 Å thick. Differentiation of the outer layer of the exocuticle, just inside the epicuticle, as an a-layer about 0.1 micron thick has more recently been established (61, 75, 79, 80–82). The relationships and terminology are shown diagrammed in Fig. 14. Figure 15 is an early electron micrograph showing the character of the enzyme-resistant endocuticle.

The medulla of animal hairs, when present, may be continuous or fragmented at the center of the fiber. Comparatively little study has been devoted to its composition (84, 85, 86) and structure (56, (87, 88). The constituent cell residues have prominent air spaces. The protein shows the β structure and is low in sulfur and resistant to alkali. These properties may illustrate an effect of deficiency of "keratinization" in the center of a structure, where access of essential materials is limited.

Electron Microscopy

Electron microscopy has greatly extended our knowledge of structural details of animal hairs. The first application of the electron microscope to this problem was initiated by Zahn (80, 90–92) in Germany in the early 1940's. In the United States, Zahn's study of fiber components was continued by Hock and McMurdie (93) in 1943. This was followed in Australia by work of Mercer, Rees, and Farrant (94–97) in 1946 and 1947; in Sweden by Olofsson (98) in 1946 and by Lindberg, Philip, Gralén, and Lagermalm (75, 77, 79, 99, 100, 101) in 1948 and afterwards; in the Netherlands by Gorter and Houwink (83) in 1948. Various workers (102, 103) devised methods of surface replication of wool and hair, leading to work of Swerdlow and Seeman (2) in 1948 and, in Australia,

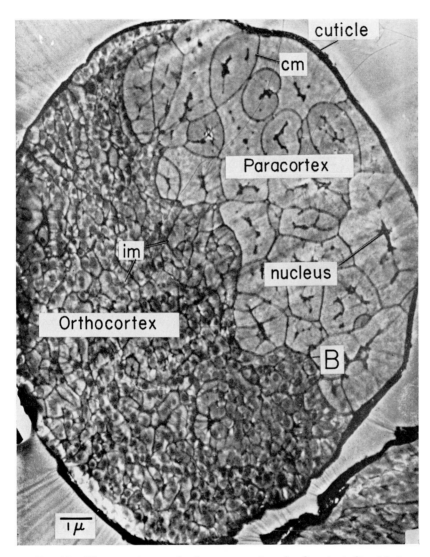

Fig. 16. Electron micrograph of a cross section of a fine Australian Merino wool fiber, showing the marked difference in texture of the macrofibrils in the fine-grained orthocortex and in the coarser paracortex [by courtesy of Dr. Rogers (34)]. B marks the boundary between the ortho and para segments. cm shows a cell membrane. im indicates "non-keratinous" material deposited among the macrofibrils.

Fig. 17. Electron micrograph of a longitudinal section of a Pindabunna Australian Merino wool fiber, reduced and treated with osmium tetroxide [from Dobb *et al.* (*61*)]. The diameter is 23 microns. Overlapping of the cuticle cells is well shown, and also, on one side, the larger "nuclear remnants" characteristic of the paracortex. Magnification: 5000 ×.

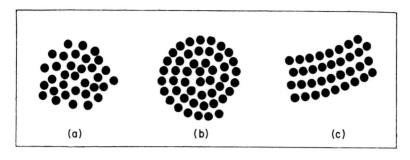

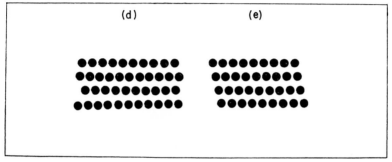

Fig. 18. (a)-(e). Diagrams illustrating the possible arrangements of microfibrils in more or less regular whorled arrays [from Fraser *et al.* (8) and Rogers (34)].

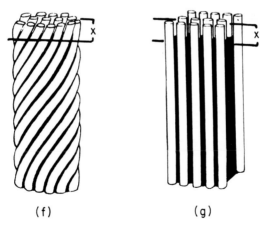

Fig. 18. (f), (g). Arrangements of microfibrils in regular parallel linear arrays. x indicates the thickness of a section taken for electron microscopy, suggesting a reason for better definition in specimens of para cortex (g) than in ortho (f).

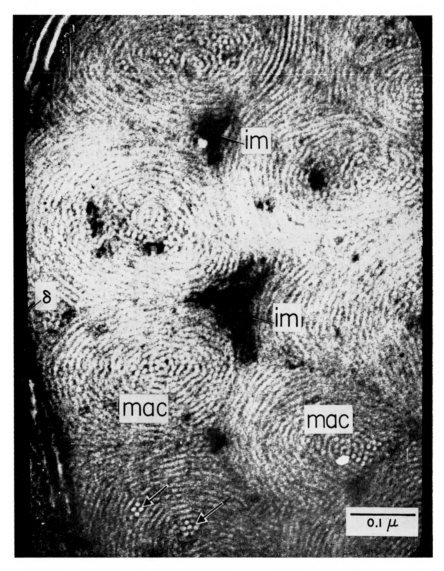

Fig. 19.   Electron micrograph showing the arrangement of microfibrils in typical orthocortex [from Rogers (5)]. This is a cross section of a rabbit guard hair, showing whorly macrofibrils (mac) partly separated by electron-dense material (im) as in the ortho segment of wool, but with a larger proportion of matrix. The arrows call attention to especially clearly delineated microfibrils, sectioned transversely, among others presumably cut obliquely.

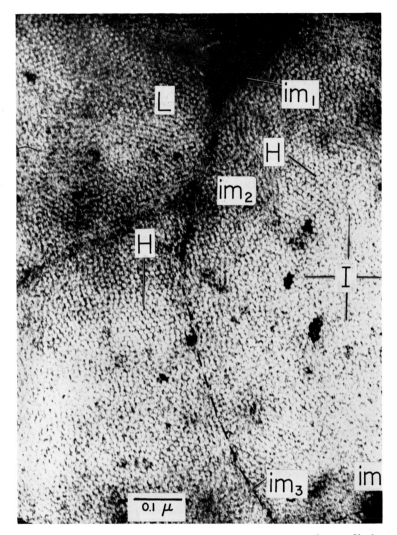

Fig. 20. Electron micrograph showing the arrangement of microfibrils in typical paracortex of Merino wool [from Rogers (34)]. The microfibrils are approximately 60 Å in diameter, set off by thinner layers of matrix, selectively stained by OsO_4 after reduction. The cross section shows hexagonal (H), layered (L), and irregular packing (I). Individual macrofibrils are partly separated by electron-dense material (im_1) in larger masses and by "flaws" (im_2 and im_3).

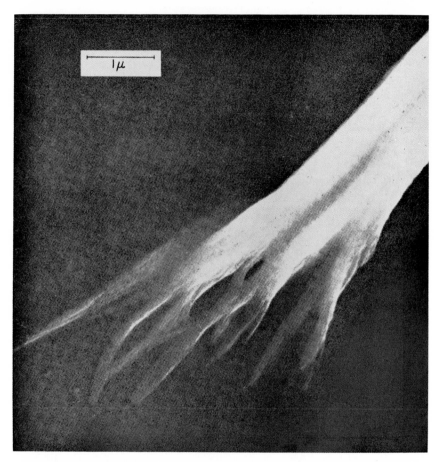

FIG. 21. Branching, fibrous tip of cortical cell fragment, about 1.25 microns in diameter, prepared by treatment with sulfuric acid and trypsin, showing subdivisions down to about 200 Å in diameter in the original electron micrograph [from Gorter and Houwink (83)].

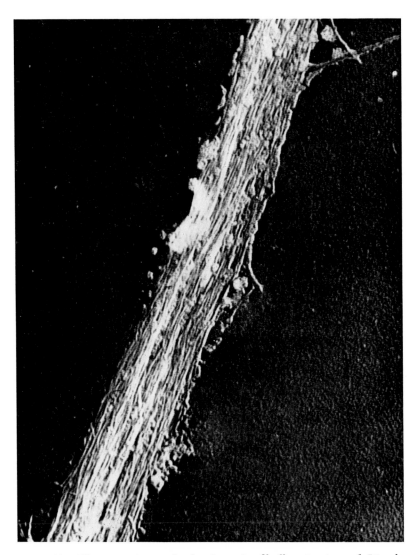

FIG. 22. Electron micrograph showing microfibrillar structure of Lincoln wool, digested with trypsin and broken up by ultrasonic vibration in 75% lithium bromide [by courtesy of Professor Sikorski; cf. (114)]. The aggregate is about 1/3 micron in diameter, while the smaller subdivisions are of the order of 80–100 Å. Magnification: 50,000 ×.

of Makinson (*104*) in 1950. More recently, work of Birbeck and Mercer (*4, 68, 82, 105–109*), Manogue and Elliott (*110–112*), and Sikorski and Woods (*9, 61, 76, 113–117*) in England, Kassenbeck (*22*) in France, and of Rogers (*5, 23, 34, 39, 70, 80, 81*) in Australia, with their respective colleagues has been especially noteworthy.

In addition to important contributions to knowledge of cuticle structure, electron microscopy has been especially successful in showing details of the cortex. An electron microscope record of a cross section of a fine wool fiber is shown in Fig. 16, and of a longitudinal section in Fig. 17. The very different macrofibrillar character of the two cortical segments is evident. The cortical cell residues are separated by membranes with at least three distinct layers. The interior of the cell is a keratinized mass of fibrillar aggregates, the macrofibrils, oriented parallel to the length of the cell. "Cytoplasmic debris" is concentrated in spaces between macrofibrils, partly serving to define their boundaries. In fibers such as fine wool, showing cortical differentiation, more of the "debris" is found in the orthocortical segment. Perhaps partly as a result, the macrofibrils in the ortho segment are smaller and better defined.

Macrofibrils are, in turn, composed of smaller microfibrils, about 60–70 Å in diameter, and about 100 Å apart, center to center, imbedded in more or less regular arrays in a non-fibrous protein matrix of high sulfur content (*5*). The microfibrils are commonly arranged in whorls in the macrofibrils of the ortho segment. Whorled arrays are uncommon in the para segment, which has some regions with nearly regular hexagonal packing. These arrangements are diagrammed in Fig. 18. Corresponding electron microscope pictures are shown as Figs. 19 and 20.

Although fibrillar structure can be discerned in both cross sections and longitudinal sections, it is also evident in the interdigitating tips of cortical cells, and is especially clearly shown in fibers macerated by appropriate chemical and enzyme treatment. Examples are shown as Figs. 21 and 22.

Fɪɢ. 23. Longitudinal section through a growing hair follicle from the human scalp, stained with Toluidine blue [from a photograph with the optical microscope by L. J. Talbert, from Montagna (*40*)]. The maximum diameter of the stained part of the bulb is about 26 microns. Actively growing cells, the nuclei of which stain most intensely, become rarer as the cells are displaced from the region near the papilla. Magnification: 260 ×.

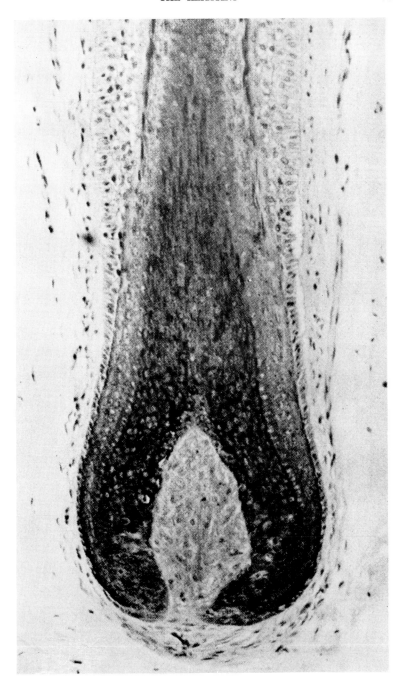

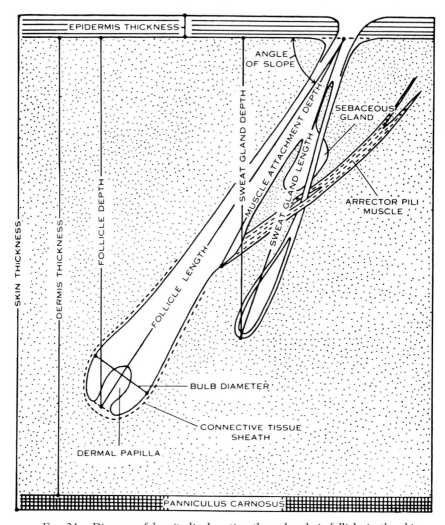

FIG. 24.   Diagram of longitudinal section through a hair follicle in the skin [from Lyne and Heidman (*118*)].

FIG. 25.   Longitudinal section through a hair follicle from the human scalp, stained to show the distribution of thiol groups [from a photograph with the optical microscope by L. J. Talbert, from Montagna (*40*)]. Magnification: 1200 ×.

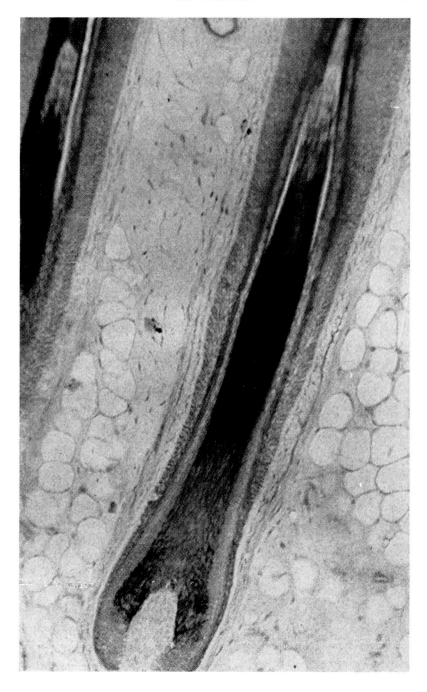

The Development of Structure

Electron microscopy has also come to the assistance of optical microscopy in studies of the development of animal hairs (*4, 82, 105–109*). The keratin-synthesizing cells form at the base of the bulb of the follicle, shown in longitudinal section in Fig. 23 and diagrammed in Fig. 24. At first these cells appear normal in cytoplasmic and nuclear equipment, complete with a nucleus, nucleoli, mitochondria, agranular vesicles similar to Golgi vesicles, and many small, dense particles 150–200 Å in diameter. Later the cells differentiate, going through characteristic changes to become cortex, cuticle, or medulla, apparently as determined by location rather than by initial differences.

The first evidence of fibril formation appears in the bulb. The process varies somewhat in detail and in timing in accordance with the cell layer concerned. In the cells that later become the cortex, filaments about 60 Å in diameter appear as loose strands at about the level of the middle of the bulb, parallel to the axis of the follicle. As these filaments increase in number at the upper end of the bulb, they become cemented into fibrils of indeterminate length and width. The cementing material appears to be a non-fibrous protein initially rich in sulfhydryl groups, which can be demonstrated histochemically, as shown in Fig. 25, in this "zone of keratinization." The fibrils in turn appear to become cemented together by a similar process. During passage out of the bulb, the cells become elongated and nearly the whole cytoplasmic space becomes packed with well-aligned fibrils and interfibrillar matrix, leaving minor amounts of residual cellular components in the interstices. The fibrous mass is strongly birefringent and the sulfhydryl groups of the fibrils and matrix become oxidized to disulfide cross links. Tests for nucleic acid, which are positive at earlier stages, become negative. The resultant spindle-shaped cortical cells are tough and horny compared with the cells in the bulb part of the follicle which are not elongated and are soft and easily crushed. The changes are summarized in Table X.

Similar processes occur in the cells which become cuticle, although the fibrillar elements are less well aligned. In this case filaments appear to be formed more directly in association with the disappearance of granular material. The whole transformation is more abrupt.

FIG. 26. Cross section of porcupine quill, reduced and stained with OsO₄, showing evidence of fine structure within the microfibrils (by courtesy of Dr. Sikorski). In this negative electron micrograph at high magnification, the microfibrils appear as irregular dark rings about 60 Å in diameter, with subdivisions of the order of 12–20 Å in diameter. Magnification: 1,120,000 ×.

81

Finally, electron microscopy presents clear evidence that the microfibrils themselves possess substructure. Examples are shown here from the work of Sikorski (Fig. 26) and Rogers (Fig. 27) with their associates. Rogers and his associates (7, 8, 23) interpret this evidence as suggesting the presence of fibrillar subunits, termed "protofibrils," each of which is suggested, from x-ray evidence (7) to be made up of three protein chains in the form of modified

TABLE X

SUMMARY OF DIFFERENCES BETWEEN THE ROOT AND SHAFT OF A WOOL FIBER
RESULTING FROM KERATINIZATION[a]

Root	Shaft
Soft and easily crushed	Tough and horny
Cells roundish	Cells elongated
Positive test for nucleic acid	Negative test for nucleic acid
Nuclei stained with hematoxylin	Nuclei unstained with hematoxylin
Cytoplasm granular in appearance	Cells distinctly fibrous
Not birefringent	Birefringent
Positive test for sulfhydryl groups	Negative test for sulfhydryl groups
No Allwörden reaction with chlorine water	Many large Allwörden "sacs"

[a] Quoted from Hock, Ramsey, and Harris (50).

α-helices. Rogers' electron microscope evidence suggests, but does not show conclusively, a structure of about 9 protofibrils surrounding a central pair, as diagrammed in Fig. 28. Such an arrangement is common in other biological fibrous systems, such as the cilia and flagella of certain protozoa and the sperm tails of various animals. A cross section of oyster sperm tails is shown in Fig. 29 as an example. If this structure can be confirmed in keratins, it will be of special interest as a possible vestige of structure used elsewhere to implement motility.

FIG. 27.   Cross section of Australian fine Merino wool stained with Pb(OH)$_2$ [by courtesy of Dr. Rogers (23)]. This detail in the para segment suggests fine structure in both microfibrils and matrix. The insert is a slightly enlarged print made from superposed print transparencies of a large number of microfibrils. It suggests a group of nine outer and two inner *proto*fibrils relatively unstained. The lower drawing is a somewhat idealized interpretation, depicting the microfibrils as circular rings of protofibrils 20 Å in diameter with a randomly oriented pair in the middle. Magnification: 1,105,000 ×.

X-Ray Diffraction: Models for the Fibrous α Component

It is now quite generally agreed that the characteristic α-keratin x-ray diffraction pattern of the animal hairs is the manifestation of

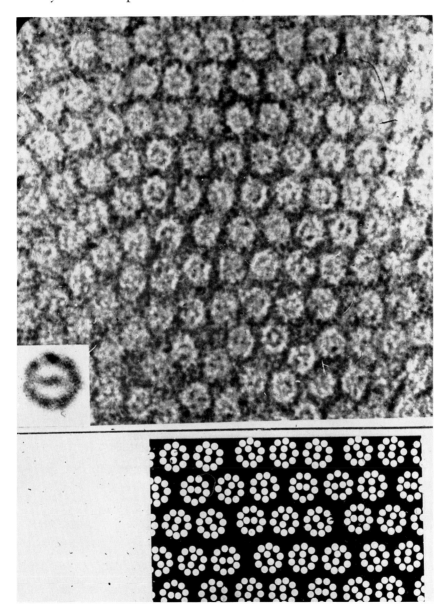

fine structure of a particular fibrous protein component or group
of related components which may be isolated as oxidized or reduced
derivatives: α-keratose (*120*) or α-kerateine (*121*), derived from
the microfibrils. The important question arises of how to relate

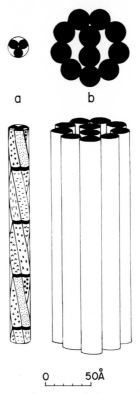

a   b

0 ____ 50Å

Fig. 28. Diagram showing features of the microfibrillar substructure of
wool suggested by electron microscope and x-ray diffraction results [from
Fraser *et al.* (*7*)]. The microfibril is shown as a circular ring of protofibrils,
with an additional central pair. The centers of the protofibrils of the outer
ring lie on a circle 60 Å in diameter. Individual protofibrils are 20 Å in diameter. Each consists of a 3-strand rope of α-helices. Each strand is regularly
divided into a repeating sequence of three distinct portions of similar length.

polypeptide composition and configuration of the α fraction with
the details of fine structure. With Rogers' suggestion of a possible
9 + 2 organization of "protofibrils" in the microfibrils, it is appropriate to inquire whether a model system of helical units can be
assembled which agrees with protein structure requirements and

gives better correspondence with the diffraction pattern of the animal hairs, and its change on stretching, than has been possible with earlier models.

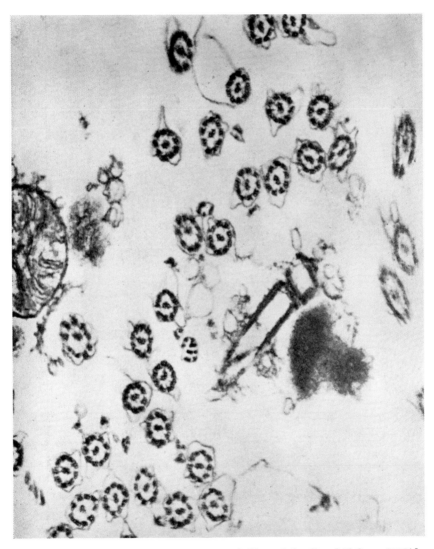

FIG. 29. Cross sections of oyster sperm tails [from Galtsoff and Philpott (119)]. The tails, about 100–150 millimicrons in diameter, provide an example of natural fibrous structures with a 9 + 2 arrangement. Magnification: 580,000 ×.

TABLE XI

X-RAY DIFFRACTION FROM KERATINS AND POLYPEPTIDES

Material and references	Equatorial reflections			Meridional reflections		
	d (Å)	Order (Indices)	Intensity	d (Å)	Order (Indices)	Intensity
α-Keratin						
Wool						
(Astbury and Woods, 1933) (11)	9.8	1	—	5.1	1	—
(Fraser and MacRae, 1957) (122)	45	2	—	—	—	—
	27	3	—	—	—	—
Porcupine quill tip						
(MacArthur, 1943) (45)	83	1	—	5.14	—	—
(Bear and Rugo, 1951) (123)	28	3	—	66.0	3	—
	45	2	—	1.5	—	—
β-Keratin						
Wool, stretched						
(Astbury and Sisson, 1935) (124)	9.8	1		3.34	2	—
	4.65	1		—	—	—
Feather						
(Corey and Wyckoff, 1936) (125)	4.68	—	S	4.90	—	S
	11.0	—	M	6.20	—	S
	33.3	—	S	23.1	—	S
	81.8	—	M	—	—	—
Cross β-keratin						
Wool, reduced in urea						
(Peacock, 1959) (126)	3.3	—	W	4.71	—	—
	10	—	—	—	—	—
	30–35	—	—	—	—	—

TABLE XI (Continued)

Material and references	Equatorial reflections			Meridional reflections		
	d (Å)	Order (Indices)	Intensity	d (Å)	Order (Indices)	Intensity
α-Polypeptide						
Poly-γ-methyl-L-glutamate	10.34	—	VVS	1.495	—	—
(Bamford et al., 1956) (127)	5.98	—	M	(5.40)	—	—
	3.89	—	M	—	—	—
(Hexagonal unit cell: a = 11.95 Å, c = 27.0 Å)						
β-Polypeptide						
Poly-γ-methyl-L-glutamate	—	—	—	3.44	—	—
(Bamford et al., 1956) (127)						
Cross β-polypeptide		(hkl)				
Poly-β-N-propyl-L-aspartate	3.32	(020 and 022)		4.76	(200)	—
(Bradbury et al., 1960) (128)	12.9	(002)				
(Monoclinic unit cell: a = 9.57 Å; b = 6.79 Å, the chain axis direction; c = 25.08 Å; β = 96°)						

A principal requirement of a model that will explain satisfactorily the observed patterns of α-keratins is that it account for characteristic spacings along the fiber axis as well as those in the perpendicular direction. Table XI summarizes the principal, characteristic results of x-ray diffraction analysis of typical keratins and synthetic polypeptides. The repeats along the fiber axis give rise to meridional spacings, including 1.5-Å and 5.1-Å spacings and those corresponding to the higher orders of an inferred 198-Å spac-

TABLE XII

SMALL ANGLE X-RAY DIFFRACTION PATTERN OF α-KERATIN[a]

(ALL MERIDIONAL OR NEAR MERIDIONAL REFLECTIONS OF SPACING GREATER
THAN 5.14 Å)

Order (k)	Spacing (d)	Intensity
3	66.3 Å	6 (medium)
4	49	1 (very weak)
5	39	2
7	27.4–27.8	4
8	24.5	2
9	22.0	2
10	19.8–19.95	4
11	18.10	3
13	15.2	1
15	13.11–13.2	1
16	12.35	4
19	10.44	3
32	6.16	m− (medium minus)

[a] The meridional or very near meridional x-ray reflections for African porcupine quill tip are given, together with approximate relative intensities and the nearest integral order of the deduced fundamental periodicity, 198 Å, from data of MacArthur (45) and Bear and Rugo (123).

ing (observed using the low angle x-ray technique, especially well in highly crystalline α-keratins such as porcupine quill tips, although only as the 3rd order [= 66.3 Å] and several higher orders including the 4th, 5th, and 7th). A more detailed list of low angle spacings observed with porcupine quill tip is given in Table XII.

Repeats perpendicular to the fiber axis give rise to equatorial spacings. Those to be accounted for in the α-keratin are 83 Å and certain higher orders of this spacing. In the case of both equatorial and meridional long spacing, the relative intensities, including absences of certain orders of the fundamental period, are significant data. This information is the basis of more detailed models to be described.

The model that accounts adequately for α-keratin structure must also account for its transformation on stretching into the more or less fully extended β-keratin structure. In the β-keratin patterns, the meridional 1.5- and 5.1-Å spacings characteristic of α-keratin are replaced by a 3.3-Å spacing due to the repeating units along the extended chain. In addition, two principal equatorial spacings appear, a 4.65-Å repeat for the backbone separation of the chains and a 9.7-Å spacing for the side-chain separation.

It was apparent soon after Pauling, Corey, and Branson (*129–131*) proposed the α-helix (Fig. 30) that this model in its simplest form does not account for some properties of the natural α-keratins (*132*). Although the α-helix does give a 1.5-Å repeat, which is the rise per residue in the helical axis direction, it does not account for the 5.1-Å spacing; instead it predicts a repeat at 5.4 Å which is the rise per 3.6 residues in the helical axis direction. The 1.5- and 5.4-Å repeats of the α-helix do account satisfactorily for spacings observed for several synthetic polypeptides. This agreement is an important step forward in the understanding of polypeptide and protein configuration. Crick (*133, 134*) made the suggestion that the natural keratins may contain α-helices, the axes of which are themselves coiled. With the proper pitch of the supercoil, it is possible to explain the meridional 5.1-Å as well as the 1.5-Å spacings and also low angle x-ray spacings. Pauling and Corey (*135*) proposed two coiled α-helical structures, shown in Fig. 31, a 3-strand rope made up of α-helices and a 7-strand cable.

Structures made up of such composite units have been designed in the first place to account for the x-ray diffraction pattern at the higher angles of diffraction, emphasizing those data most regularly observed. The keratin structure is so complex that, as with other proteins, direct analysis is practically impossible. Instead, progress has been made by inventing plausible models, taking into account as much of the available evidence as possible, and checking the models against the x-ray data. The main difficulties encountered in designing such models are the need to account satisfactorily not only for the x-ray data, but also for the keratin density, for reversible, approximately two-fold extension in the α-β transformation, and for biological assembly. The measured density of dry keratins is commonly in the range 1.27–1.34 (*136*). Ordinarily the crystalline portion of such material would be expected to have a slightly higher density than the average, perhaps 1.39 as has been suggested. However, keratins are chemically heterogeneous. Inasmuch as the high sulfur component, which—other factors being the same —would have a density higher than average, has been assigned to

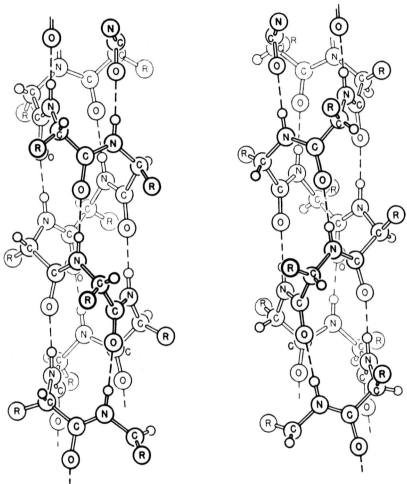

Fɪɢ. 30.   Drawings showing the characteristic arrangement of atoms in the α-helix [from Corey and Pauling (158)]. Right- and left-hand forms are shown. The former is the usual naturally occurring form. However, the pitch and number of residues per turn may be subject to adjustment to accommodate various side chains of the different amino acid residues. Although several synthetic polypeptides have been clearly shown to occur as α-helices, the x-ray diffraction patterns of α-keratins indicate that a somewhat modified form or packing arrangement is needed to account for their structure.

the amorphous region, the density predicted by a model is not directly comparable with the average density.

The problem of the α-β transformation is that of taking into account restraints resulting from primary cross-linking and from entwining, in the case of rope or cable models, in such a way as to permit the observed extension. It is also desirable to accommodate a reasonable process for the natural formation of keratin. In spite of evidence that nucleic acids and collagen have twisted structures,

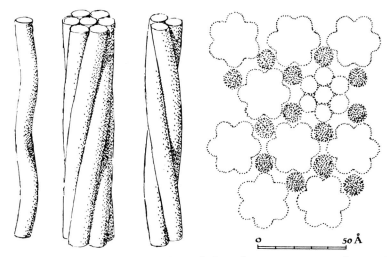

FIG. 31. The compound α-helix and derived structures proposed as units for α-keratin [from Pauling and Corey (135)]. Left: the α-helix, shown as its cylindrical envelope, deformed into a superhelix. Aggregates of coiled helices to make a 7-strand cable and 3-strand rope are shown. At the right, a packing diagram of 7-strand cables and straight helices is shown to suggest ways of achieving lateral order with a long enough period to account for the longer equatorial x-ray diffraction spacings.

it is hard to accept as reasonable a process of formation requiring twisting together strands of indefinite length, especially if these include different but similar units put together in a highly specific way. The related problems of demonstrating possible helical structure on the microfibril and showing details of its formation are on the borderline of resolution by electron microscopy, and therefore pose a special challenge to electron microscopists. As an alternative to twisting, Mercer (4), in particular, has discussed evidence that natural fibers of both the KMEF and collagen groups are formed naturally by linear association of small "corpuscular" units. However, we do not need to suppose that the "corpuscles" are approximately spherical, provided that they are small enough. Nor is it necessary that their shape be maintained in the final structure. Furthermore, association is not exclusively linear, since lateral as well as axial ordering is evident. If the units are short enough, an extended helical aggregate, even in the form of a plied rope or cable, may be built up by slight modification of end-to-end aggregation without twisting. Our understanding of this aspect of structure is now heavily dependent on analysis of low angle x-ray diffraction, disclosing long periodicities in both axial and lateral directions that are somewhat more dependent on the nature and history of the particular keratin studied than is the high angle pattern.

Two aspects of keratin structure have been somewhat clarified by analysis of the low angle equatorial diffraction pattern: the shape and spacing of the diffracting units and certain features of their internal structure. Taking into account not only the pattern given by the keratin, but also changes due to uptake of water and various metals, Fraser and MacRae (137) have related the x-ray diffracting structure to the microfibrillar structure seen by electron microscopy. By their analysis, the equatorial diffraction pattern of α-keratins is that of parallel cylindrical scattering units, not necessarily round in cross section, about 70 Å in average diameter and arranged in layers, at intervals of about 86 Å, in which the units are aligned but not ordinarily in register with those of adjoining layers. The layers may be relatively straight, curved, or concentric. Absence of discrete low angle scattering in poorly ordered keratins such as epidermis, horn, and hoof, is evidence that scattering from the fibrillar units of such substances is independent, although the size of the units is similar (42). Lateral order is favored by a certain amount of water, just as in more crystalline proteins.

Some features of the internal structure of the scattering units have also been determined from the equatorial long spacings. The equatorial diffraction of the more crystalline α-keratins can be accounted for as that of a group of irregularly close-packed α-helices. Simple, *regular packing* of small fibrillar units such as single helices or of 3-strand ropes within the microfibril seems to be excluded, but the data may be compatible with a regular arrangement of 7-strand cables or other structures built up of four or more helices, for example the 9 + 2 arrangement, which although more or less specific may not be geometrically regular.

To summarize the evidence from equatorial diffraction of x-rays, α-keratins are made up of cylindical fibrillar units, identified with the microfibrils seen by electron microscopy. The internal structure of these fibrils, deduced also from high angle diffraction, is based on α-helices, the axes of which are inclined somewhat to the axes of the individual fibrils. The helices are either irregularly arranged or are grouped in a way more complicated than simple hexagonal packing. The inclination of the helical axis is inferred to account for the axial spacing, 5.1 Å, shorter than that, 5.4 Å, for the α-helix constructed with atomic distances and angles observed in simple amino acid derivatives and confirmed for certain synthetic polypeptides. To account for observation of the 5.1-Å reflection as meridional, rather than off-axis, the radial component of the axial inclination must be balanced, as in rope or cable models, or randomized in direction.

At least four packing patterns compatible with larger-scale regularity have been proposed. One is the 7-strand cable already cited (135), which can account for the 28-Å equatorial diffraction maximum, but not for longer periodicity unless further assumptions are made of larger-scale association. About five or six such cables would be needed to make up the observed scattering unit, with several additional polypeptide chains to fill in spaces between the cables to adjust the density. Swanbeck (138) has proposed a model, diagrammed in Fig. 32, that is essentially an elaboration of the cable idea. This model is a concentrically layered structure centered on a group of three. The tilt of the layers increases toward the outside, perhaps reaching a condition of limiting stability that limits the fibrillar size. The number of helices in each layer is directly related to an observed order of scattering in the x-ray diagram.

A third, quite different long-range structure, diagrammed in Fig. 33, has been proposed by Huggins (139, 140). This is based on association of compound helical units in threes at successive levels of organization until the long-range periodicity is large enough. To allow convenient α-β transformation, the units are not entwined, but combined first of all in cross-linked triads. The members of a triad are distinguishable by orientation of, for example, the cross-linking groups. The triads are in turn regularly hydrogen-bonded to form groups of nine, in which each triad is distinguishable by the relative orientation of its members. In this way a regular structure is built up to form a unit cell containing 81 chains, large enough to account for the largest equatorial periodicity. This model was developed before the proposal of

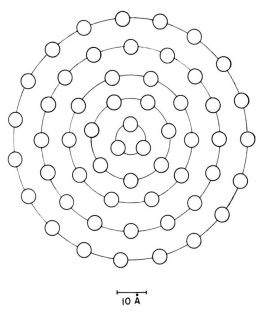

10 Å

FIG. 32. Packing diagram of a model proposed by Swanbeck (138) for α-keratin of a tonofilament or microfibril. Each circle represents a protein chain in the form of an α-helix in cross section. The model is designed to account for the most prominent layer lines (numbers 3, 7, 10, 16, and 19) shown by porcupine quill tip at low and moderate angles of diffraction. Radii of the concentric layers are estimated to be 5, 13, 20.5, 28.5, and 38 Å. The angles of tilt between the fiber axis and the axes of the α-helices in successive layers progress from 9° to 50°. The diameter as shown is close to 80 Å, in reasonable agreement with electron microscopy, and may be adjusted to accommodate an observed apparent increase in diameter during keratinization in human skin (6).

Fraser and MacRae (137) to account for long spacing by an array of cylindrical units in a matrix, but it also provides a way of packing individual helices very regularly, yet still accounting for the observed long-range equatorial periodicity. The model is also easily adapted to packing 3-strand ropes. In addition, Huggins introduces the possibility that the twisting of a rope need not be continuous, but may be in segments with successive segments superposed axially. This feature facilitates extension to give the α-β transformation and provides a basis for accounting for axial periodicity.

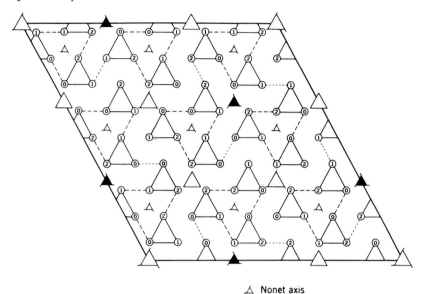

△ Nonet axis

▲ 27-chain axis

△ △ Axes centering three 27-chain groups

Fig. 33. Packing diagram of a model for α-keratin proposed by Huggins (139, 140). Each circle represents a protein chain in the form of an α-helix in cross section. The numbers (0, 1, 2) designate three classes of chains displaced axially with respect to one another by increments of one-third of a unit distance. The dotted lines indicate patterns of orientation established by chemical interaction between corresponding groups of atoms. The structure provides regularity of packing compatible with long-range periodicity in lateral and axial directions. It can be adapted to accommodate 3-strand ropes.

A fourth, most recent, proposal concerning internal structure of the microfibrils is the 9 + 2 arrangement suggested by electron microscope evidence (23).

Having reviewed structural inferences made with the help of the x-ray equatorial diffraction pattern, we now consider in more detail the evidence provided by the low angle meridional diffraction pattern. This evidence permits deduction of a fundamental periodicity of 198 Å in the direction of the fibrillar axis. This length of supercoiled α-helix accommodates about 144 amino acid residues, with a molecular weight of about 17,000 as a single-strand unit. An associated group of three, as in models based on a 3-strand rope (including the 9 + 2 model) or triads, would then have unit weights near 50,000, while a cyclic unit of this length, suggested for example by Crewther and Dowling (37), would have a unit weight of about 33,000. Keratin protein derivatives of widely varying molecular weight have been reported. In some cases, substantial components of molecular weight 30,000 or higher have been reported, but lack of evidence of homogeneity and difficulties of measurement preclude convincing support to a unit of any precise molecular weight.

X-ray spacings at fractions of the fundamental period are also observed, but not all possible orders. The relative intensities of these higher order spacings are the basis for inferring longitudinal structure within the scattering unit. As with equatorial spacings, further information has been sought from changes occurring as a result of water uptake and treatment with heavy elements such as silver and iodine. Further evidence from this technique is to be expected.

A strong meridional spacing at 66 Å, one-third of the inferred fundamental period, is considered specially significant. It may be accounted for by a periodic discontinuity in the longitudinal structure associated with a characteristic variation in electron density. Referred back to an α-helical unit this suggests a periodic discontinuity every 48 amino acid residues, separating portions that are very similar, but not completely identical. Such periodicity may result from a repeating chemical sequence, or to features such as variation in perfection of packing because of bulky side chains, for example, the presence of cross-linking sites, or the occurrence of a proline residue, which is recognized as incompatible with local α-helical structure for geometrical reasons.

A discussion by Huggins (141) also suggests that the extent of regularity of packing of a fundamental polymer unit such as the α-helix may be governed by forces such as side-chain interaction by a more general mechanism. It is proposed that forces between the crystallizing units result in slight deformation of the aggregate. As an illustration, we may imagine that two straight α-helixes undergoing side-by-side aggregation may be constrained to twist somewhat about their common axis. An aggregate of such units would be stressed and tend to be deformed. When the deformation reaches a limiting value, there will be an abrupt readjustment in structure to relieve the accumulating stress. In the case of the helices, we picture the forces of association of the helices to result also in stress on the internal hydrogen bonding, tending to maintain the original minimally stressed form. When the total amount of twist accumulated longitudinally from an unconstrained reference point, such as a free end, is great enough, there will be a break, either in the regular sequence of interactions joining the two chains, or in the internal bonding of the chains in such a way as to relieve the stress. In the case of keratins, evidence must be obtained to determine the extent to which such a mechanism may operate. As Huggins points out, keratin long spacing may also result from regular axial and radial displacement of a repeating pattern of amino acid residues in going from one line of residues to the next.

Specific models based on ideas of periodic discontinuities in helical structure have been discussed by Fraser and MacRae (7, 142, 143). These are modifications of the 3-strand rope of α-helices and have been tested by the optical transform method for agreement with the low angle x-ray diffraction pattern. In one model, the three strands are interrupted simultaneously at intervals of 66 Å by a major change in electron density in such a way that each strand consists of a regular sequence of three similar but not identical units. The same model would appear to represent equally well either a group of entwined, interrupted helical segments or one in which the discontinuity permitted successive segments of the same polypeptide chain to be superposed axially, as suggested by Huggins (139).

Fraser and MacRae also consider a more open model, a 3-strand, segmented rope in which the segments are straight sections of α-helices, close-packed at their points of contact midway between the joints. The angle of inclination of the individual segments is proposed to be about 10° from the axial direction, in order to permit optimum packing of adjoining units and to give a low angle diffraction pattern, tested by the optical transform method, similar to the pattern given by keratin. Examples of this study are shown in Fig. 34.

An abrupt change in helix direction is now very commonly postu-

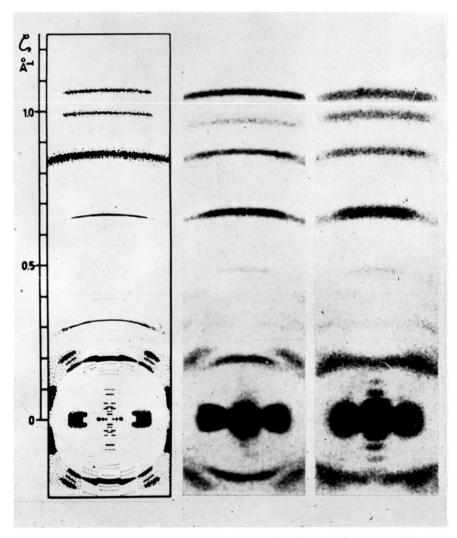

FIG. 34. Development of attempts to account for the complete x-ray diffraction pattern of α-keratin as made up of modified 3-strand ropes [from Fraser *et al.* (*7*) and Fraser and MacRae (*143*)]. From left to right are shown: a drawing of the prominent features of the x-ray diffraction pattern of well-ordered α-keratin, porcupine quill tip; a reconstruction, by means of the optical transform method, of the diffraction pattern of the 3-strand rope model according to Crick (*134*); and the corresponding reconstruction of the diffraction pattern of a segmented rope. The segmented model tested differs from that shown in Fig. 28 in having the strands made up of straight sections of α-helix, 20–30 Å long and inclined at 10° to the fibril axis. The length and inclination of the segments are selected to give the best packing of aggregates and to give an optical transform most nearly in agreement with the x-ray pattern.

98

lated to result from occurrence of a proline residue in the poly-peptide chain. For example, Crewther and Dowling (37) have recently proposed a keratin structural unit in which two proline residues separated by one or two other residues permit reversal of the axis direction with a displacement of about 10 Å, making possible a cyclic polypeptide unit with parallel strands in the α configuration. If the sense of the helix is not reversed, Crewther and Dowling estimate the change in direction of the helical axis due to a single proline group to be 30°.

The evidence for a possible cyclic polypeptide unit (144) is that polypeptide end-groups have not been detected in quantity suffi-cient to account for the molecular weight of solubilized proteins. Furthermore, the ones that are detected are those most easily formed by hydrolysis. The same evidence may also mean, however, that keratin has easily hydrolyzed or nonconventional chain ends.

In summing up information about the fibrous component of α-keratin, we select evidence, interpretation, and principles that seem to us most pertinent and develop still another model, which will have various features of those already described. We face the universal problem of trying to account for as many facts as possible without introducing specific detail not required by the evidence. At the same time we wish to emphasize the place of certain evi-dence—that of chemical composition—which will almost certainly be modified by further study. It seems to us that the microfibrillar protein has substantial portions formed into α-helical segments about 66 Å long (as projected on the fiber axis) separated by chemical and structural discontinuities. Segments of adjoining chains are approximately aligned, with an average inclination to the fiber axis determined by comparing the observed fundamental axial spacing with that of presumed axially aligned α-helices. The units will be overlapped in such a way as to provide continuity of fibrillar structure, and may be grouped provisionally to accord with features of other proposed models.

In developing the model in more detail, we consider first the amino acid composition of isolated α-keratose, which may be taken to approximate that of the microfibrillar protein except for oxida-tion. This has been summarized by Crewther and Dowling (37) as already shown in Table VIII. These data show histidine present in smallest amount, 0.48 residues per 10,000 gm. Noting that the calculation is likely to be modified by preparation and analysis of fractions of more clearly established homogeneity, we calculate the molecular weight of the fundamental unit to be at least 20,000 (with at least one histidine residue). This would correspond to a total of 172 residues, assuming a mean residue weight of 116. On this basis, the number of proline residues per molecule approximates six. It is necessary to consider proline in setting up a helical

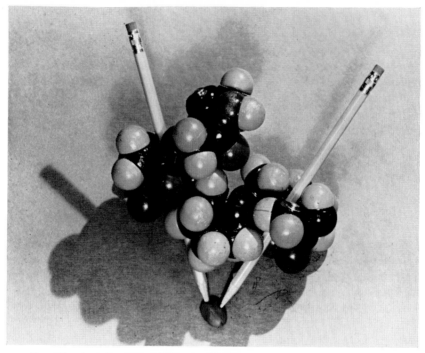

Fig. 35. A Fisher-Hirschfelder model of part of a polypeptide chain, illustrating the change in direction of the α-helical axis resulting from the presence of a proline residue.

model for α-keratose, because proline's exceptional ring structure imposes limits to the continuity of a helix. At the same time it is recognized that a discontinuity can occur without intervention of a proline residue. Using atom models, as in Fig. 35, we estimate that the presence of a single proline residue in a helix causes a deflection of the helix axis, which approximates 20°. This is to be compared with the 30° estimated by Crewther and Dowling (37) and the 10° tilt in a Fraser and MacRae model (7, 143).

For the present we do not know the position of the 6 proline residues in α-keratose. However, by assigning positions, it is possible to construct a segmented helix model for α-keratose, which can be fitted by "aggregation" with similar units into a "super"-structure whose dimensions and repeat characteristics are in accord with the principal x-ray and electron microscope evidence. As pointed out, a principal feature of the x-ray diffraction pattern of α-keratins is the axial 5.1-Å repeat, whereas the prototype of α-helix

TABLE XIII
α-Helix Parameters

Residues (Per repeat)	Turns (Per repeat)	Residues (Per turn)
11	3	3.67
15	4	3.75
18	5	3.60
48	13	3.693

The 3.693-residue α-helix as a possible keratin component

13 Turns × 3.693 residues per turn = 48 residues per segment
13 Turns × 5.1 Å per turn = 66.3 Å per segment
3 × 66.3 Å = 198.9 Å per repeating unit
3 × 48 = 144 residues per repeating unit
144 × 116 mean residue weight = 16,700 molecular weight per repeat distance
(172 × 116 = 20,000)

structure gives a repeat close to 5.4 Å. It is possible to account for the difference by assuming that α-helices are present in α-keratins as an aggregate of segmented protein molecules whose segments are tilted away from the principal axis of the microfibril to the extent that will give a 5.1-Å rather than the 5.4-Å x-ray repeat pattern. This requires a tilt of approximately 20°, the angle whose cosine is 5.1/5.4. Assignment of a proline residue between segments in the fiber axis direction makes possible a succession of segments with the same tilt but differently oriented. Either a random or balanced orientation of the equatorial projection of the segments is required to assure truly meridional x-ray diffraction.

An idea of the length of segments present in the principal axis direction is obtained from a second feature of the x-ray diffraction pattern of α-keratins. This is the prominent meridional reflection that corresponds to a repeat pattern in the fiber axis direction of 66 Å. Actually this repeat is, as already noted, the third order of a repeat of 198 Å that is not generally observed. A repeating unit with a whole number of amino acid residues is easily accommodated in this distance. As seen from Table XIII, the 3.693-residue α-helix gives a repeat pattern every 13 turns of this helix. Since

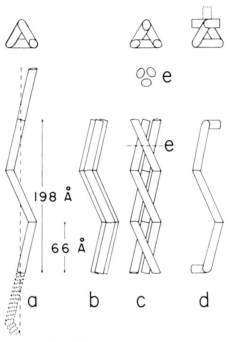

FIG. 36. The segmented α-helix and its aggregates. At the left, *a*, an α-helix is represented as divided into segments, here suggested to be about 70 Å long, accounting for a repeating distance of 66 Å in the axial direction. Fraser and MacRae (*143*) suggest a shorter segment. The angle between segments is adjusted to account for the apparent difference between the spacing of turns of α-helices in synthetic polypeptides and in keratins. Parallel and 3-strand twisted aggregates are shown in *b* and *c*, roughly corresponding in diameter to protofibrils. A unit three segments long matches the inferred fundamental x-ray periodicity. Present analytical results suggest that this length is not quite enough to accommodate the average molecular unit. To allow for this excess, short tails as suggested in *d*, may be added.

each turn, in the case of a tilted helix, corresponds to a rise in the microfibril axis direction of 5.1 Å the 13-turn repeat will occur every 66.3 (13 × 5.1) Å, including 48 residues. Thus we may consider the "molecule" of protein making up the α structure to have

3 segments approximately aligned with the fiber axis, but bent about 20° between segments because of the presence of a proline residue between each pair of adjoining segments. This would require 2 proline residues; the remaining 4 proline residues may conceiv-

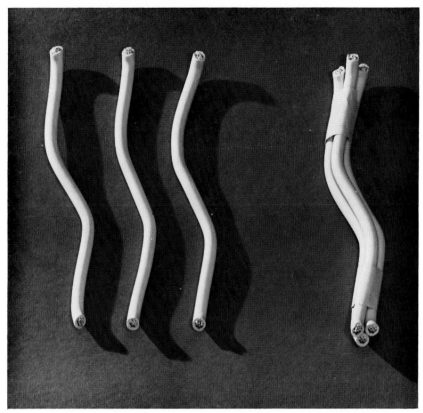

Fig. 37. A model, from electricians' cable, of an α-keratin unit of molecular weight about 20,000, with three principal segments each about 66 Å long as measured in the direction of the fiber axis. A parallel bundle of three is also shown.

ably define the ends of the 3-segment structure. The length in the fiber axis direction of the 3-segment helix structure will be 198.9 Å (3 × 66.3 Å) in reasonable agreement with the observed 198-Å repeat typical of α-keratins. Such a 3-segment structure will contain 144 (3 × 13 × 3.693) amino acid residues, 28 residues less than the 172 residues in the α-keratose derivative presumed to have a molecular weight of 20,000. The extra 28 residues may lie tilted out of the fiber axis with the help of the additional proline residues spaced at 198 Å. A segmented helix having this shape is shown

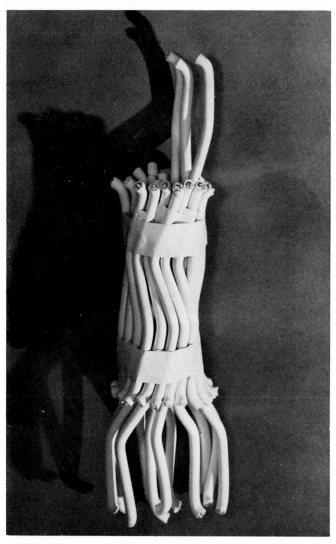

FIG. 38.   Model of a microfibril made up of units shown in Fig. 37, illustrating one way in which short, 3-segment units can be assembled into a continuous fibrillar structure.

in Fig. 36, and a model constructed to scale using electricians
cable (approximately 7 million to 1) is shown in Fig. 37. Three
of these unit molecule models can be "associated" conveniently,
as shown in the figure, to account for the protofibril of Rogers or
other 3-stranded substructural unit. Moreover, 9 such protofibril
models can be arranged around 2 in the center to give a model
for a 9 + 2 arrangement.

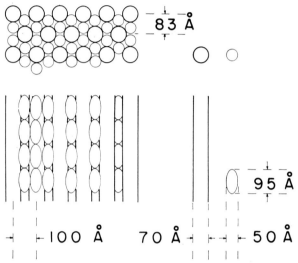

FIG. 39. Drawing, idealized, illustrating the arrangement and dimensions
of keratin microfibrils in a structured matrix [various details after Mercer (4),
Sikorski and Woods (9), and Rogers (34)]. The matrix is described as
pseudoglobular and as including components, not distinguished in the drawing, both high and low in sulfur.

By staggering placement of the units it is possible to construct
a continuous microfibrillar structure as shown in Fig. 38. When
made with 33 units in a cross section, the approximate model (from
electricians' cable) suggests a microfibril diameter near 80 Å. This
is about 10–15% larger than compatible with the major equatorial
x-ray spacing, 83 Å, for α-keratin, because of the need for space
to incorporate an approximately equal proportion of matrix. However, it is likely that this discrepancy would be largely resolved
by using a more pliable material for constructing the model.

Although this model is at best a very rough approximation, it may
serve to encourage appropriate questions and guide the search for

missing information. A more complete description of the structure of various keratins at all levels of organization will come as further knowledge is obtained of the properties, composition, and amino acid sequences of specific polypeptide components. Substantial progress toward this goal is being made.

Non-fibrous Components: the Matrix

In the preceding discussion detailed attention has centered on the fibrous elements of structure because these are responsible for the characteristic x-ray diffraction pattern. Calculation from rela-

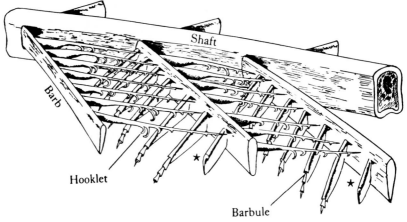

FIG. 40.   Stereogram showing the structure of a representative feather [from Storer (147)]. Stars (★) indicate two proximal barbules cut to show curved edge along which hooklets slide to make feather flexible.

tive areas in the electron microscope records suggests that the microfibrils constitute only 30–45% of the keratin structure. These values may be compared with estimates of 20–35% for the crystalline fractions of wool or porcupine quill tip based on relative densities (136). Appropriate allowance for minor histological components and for membranes leaves a substantial fraction to be accounted for as matrix. This phase is identified with the high sulfur α-keratose fraction (Table VIII), which is of relatively low molecular weight.

Crewther and Dowling (37) have discussed the relationship of the structure and chemical composition of the matrix. They suggest the possibility that the matrix is made up of more or less globular molecules containing short α-helical segments, alternately right-

and left-hand, joined by proline residues, and with many cystine cross-links between residues in the same polypeptide chain. However the average content of proline is so high—one in eight residues in the high sulfur protein fraction from wool—that an appreciable α-helical content seems unlikely. For such a structure it would be necessary to group the proline residues extensively, and perhaps also the cystine, to get long enough uninterrupted helix-forming sequences.

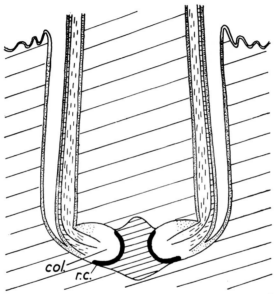

Fig. 41. Diagram of the feather follicle with growing calamus [from Rudall (10), after Lillie (145)], simplified to show the relative occurrence of feather β-keratin, indicated by short dashed lines, and α-keratin, dotted. The collar (col.), is a region of active cell division corresponding to the bulb of a hair follicle. Regeneration cells (r.c.), at its base, initiate feather growth.

Although the matrix is described as amorphous, structural regularities in it are suggested by the uptake of silver or other heavy elements under favorable conditions through effects on x-ray diffraction and especially on the appearance under the electron microscope. According to Sikorski and Woods (9), silver produces in the matrix clear evidence of a longitudinal repeat of approximately 95 Å: "The appearance of the matrix is pseudoglobular with units approximately 50 Å across." A diagram of the combined structure suggested is given in Fig. 39.

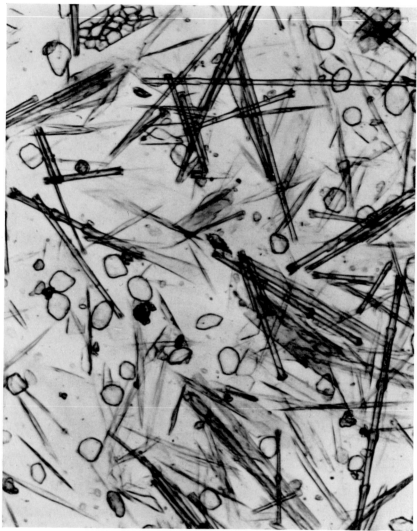

Fig. 42. Structural elements released from chicken contour feathers by papain digestion include barbule fragments, medullary cells, and spindle-shaped cortical cells similar to those obtainable from hairs (photograph with the optical microscope by F. T. Jones). Magnification: 230 ×.

Feather Keratin

In complexity of structure, feather is the most highly developed keratin product. Feather structure and its development have been described by Lillie (*145*). A typical feather consists of a translucent calamus or quill, embedded in the skin, a shaft, and a vane.

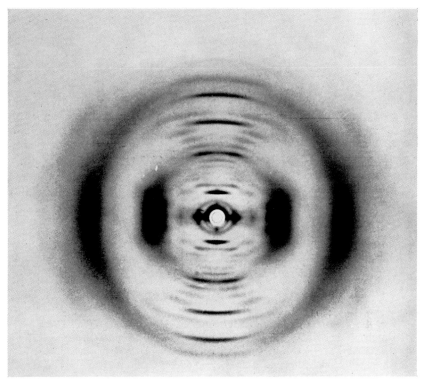

FIG. 43. X-ray diffraction pattern of turkey feather calamus, an example of unusually well-ordered β-keratin [from Schor and Krimm (*152*)].

The calamus is one to several millimeters wide. An opaque, mostly hollow shaft continues from the calamus for a few to 20 or more centimeters, except in down, which may have no shaft. The vane is made up of flattened, elongated branches, the barbs, forming regular rows on opposite sides of the shaft. The barbs are further branched into barbules (Fig. 40), which may be flattened or elongated, with hooks, knobs, and other structural detail characteristic of the species and of the feather tract on the bird. The fine structure is often so regular and with so large a periodicity that the feather appears colored or iridescent as a consequence of optical interference (*146*). The structure underlying these colors was clarified in part with the help of the electron microscope (*148*). The more striking differences from mammalian hair, apart from the much greater size and complexity of development of feather, are

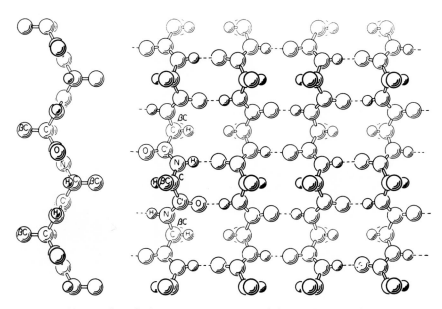

FIG. 44. A pleated sheet structure, proposed by Pauling *et al.* (*153*), is the probable basis of the feather keratin and other β-keratin structures. The protein chains are not quite fully extended, but "pleated" in such a way as to allow optimum hydrogen bonding of adjoining chains and to accommodate side chains. As in the case of the α-helix, the exact relationships may be modified by the character of the side chains. In this example, as confirmed for silk fibroin, adjoining chains are anti-parallel, running in opposite directions. This basic structure gives an axial repeat of 6.50 Å. Parallel chains, running in the same direction, provide a slightly longer repeat, 7.00 Å.

the much greater incorporation of air spaces, the preponderant occurrence of keratin in the β form, a lower content of cystine and higher contents of serine and proline, for example, and a lower average polypeptide chain weight. The change from the α pattern may be directly related to the higher content of proline, which interferes with the α-helical structure. The calamus may differ appreciably from the rest of the feather in composition and chemical properties such as solubility (20, 149).

Like hair, a feather grows from a follicle, diagrammed in Fig. 41. In the growth of feather, the main portion is formed in the β configuration but there are definite minor portions, notably the surface layer, which have the α configuration as indicated in the diagram.

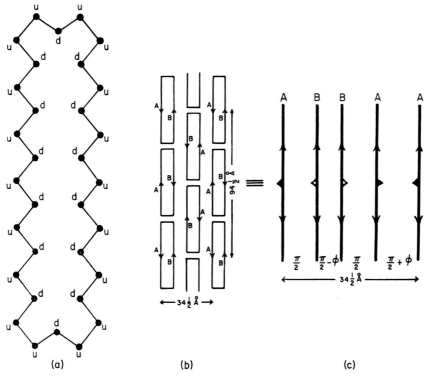

(a)   (b)   (c)

Fig. 45. Diagram of feather structure proposed by Astbury and Beighton (154). A cyclic polypeptide unit (a) is proposed to account for the absence of detectable end-groups. α-Carbon atoms are indicated by dots. Directions of bonds to β-carbon atoms are indicated by u (up) and d (down). The size and arrangement of the units is planned to conform to the net pattern determined by Bear and Rugo (123), as shown in (b). An equivalent arrangement of chains shown in (c) was used to determine the equatorial intensities of the x-ray diffraction pattern. π and φ define the x-ray phase angles. Occurrence of proline residues is proposed to polarize the structure. Regularity in the direction perpendicular to the network is much restricted. Limitation of association of the units (molecular weight about 3500) may perhaps be compatible with Woodin's (157) measurements on solubilized protein, givin a molecular weight of 11,000.

As in the case of wool, chicken feathers have a cuticular layer of flattened cells (*150*) which have been shown to have a very thin chemically resistant surface layer, the epicuticle. In the feather this shows many conical projections (*151*). Partial enzyme digestion of chicken or duck feathers releases spindle-shaped cortical

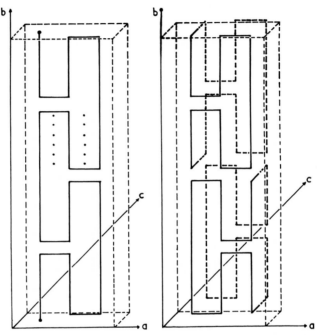

Fig. 46.   Diagram of feather structures proposed by Fraser and MacRae (*155*). Left: an example of how a protein chain of about 10,000 molecular weight, 300 Å long, can be accommodated in an orthogonal unit cell 34 × 95 × 4.7 Å. The grid of 12 dots indicates a small region of regular β structure. Right: a closely similar structure accommodating cyclic units of the same molecular weight. In each case, side chains extend in the direction of the a-axis. Hydrogen bonding is in the direction of the c-axis. The structure is supported in part by test with optical transforms.

cells as in the case of wool, but in addition a great variety of cuboidal or polyhedral cells (which may be air-filled) and barbule segments (Fig. 42). In association with its different chemical composition and lower polypeptide chain weight, feather is more soluble than wool or other keratins in typical keratin solvents, such as concentrated urea with a reducing agent, and it differs quite strikingly in its characteristic solubility in hot aqueous alcohol (with a reducing agent).

Feather has not been characterized so well as hair with the electron microscope, but recent unpublished work of Rogers indicates

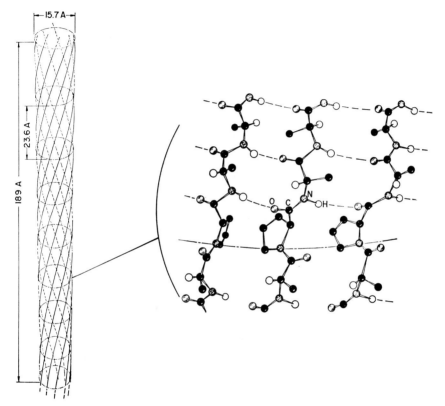

FIG. 47. "β-Helix" model proposed for the structure of feather by Schor and Krimm (156). The ordered component of feather keratin is proposed to have proline residues distributed periodically, one in every eight, along noncyclic polypeptide units. In part because of the proline residues, the chains are assigned a long pitch helical conformation with a period of 189 Å, a distance of 23.6 Å between proline residues, and an average distance of 2.96 Å per amino acid residue in the axial direction. The helices are right-handed, with proline rings on the inside. Ten chains are proposed to be associated to form a cylindrical unit. The cylinders are proposed to be packed in cables of seven to account for the equatorial x-ray diffraction periodicities. The model takes into account a wide variety of evidence, but is not in detailed agreement with some of it.

that feather keratin is also made up of small filaments of the order of 50–100 Å in diameter, but that these are not grouped in units like those of the α-keratins.

X-ray analysis of feather has yielded remarkably detailed diffraction patterns, such as that shown in Fig. 43. These have led to several hypothetical structures to account for the various features. Among these may be noted models of arrangements of large units (123) and, on a finer scale, the pleated sheet structures of Pauling, Corey and Branson (153), shown in Fig. 44, structures of folded, e.g. cyclic, peptide units recently suggested by Astbury and Beighton (154) (Fig. 45) and by Fraser and MacRae (155) (Fig. 46), and a multi-chain helix, by Schor and Krimm (156) (Fig. 47). The x-ray patterns show that feather structure is often highly ordered and almost certainly closely related to the pleated sheet structures. In developing more precise hypotheses, attention has been focused on the relatively low molecular weight, 11,000, of solubilized feather protein (157) and its apparent absence of end-groups, suggesting a cyclic polypeptide unit.

SUMMARY

The Relationship of the Various Keratins

It is desirable to summarize these observations by attempting a unifying description, or at least by suggesting principles by which the whole can be more closely related. In the evolution of keratin, the crucial biological step is the change from cell division (in the surface layer) with the dividing plane perpendicular to the surface, to division with the plane parallel to the surface. As a result cells come to be displaced away from their source of nourishment into a lethal environment. As the displaced cells perish, protein synthesis is one of the last functions to be destroyed. As a result, the dying cells accumulate a relatively large proportion of protein.

The proteins, as they are concentrated, aggregate in characteristic ways, governed by their composition, molecular weight, and properties of the environment such as the proportions of different proteins and other constituents, relative rates of formation and drying, access of oxygen and oxidation catalysts, and gradients of salt and pH.

As polypeptides, many proteins tend to assume a particular helical form, internally hydrogen-bonded, with a tendency toward ordered parallel aggregation in concentrated sytsems. Individual molecular units may have specific, modified, for example, kinked shapes. The exact manner of aggregation is modified by details of composition. In particular, twisted aggregates may form at various levels of organization. Thus we deduce the occurrence of α-helices, postulate rope, cable, or other combinations of helices or modified helices, and observe microfibrils (with substructure) spaced in a structured, but less well-ordered matrix. In some cases the microfibrils are poorly ordered, but in others they form whorls or straight arrays making up the larger fiber domains of macrofibrils. The size, spacing, uniformity, and perfection of packing of these fibrous aggregates will be governed by factors such as the proportions of components which are not completely compatible, the fit of the units, and the rate of drying.

In skin keratin, the relatively simple geometry of growth and drying result in cells flattened in their direction of displacement toward the surface. This process results in partial orientation of the fibrous aggregates, so that they lie more or less parallel to the surface, but not usually parallel to one another. The low degree of order is also related to a relatively high proportion of lipid and to relatively rapid growth and hardening.

Other keratin structures are formed by modifications of the skin. Two especially significant features have been pointed out, considering the follicle forming a hair or wool fiber as typical. These are, first, a source of intense localized growth and, second, provision for introducing additional components somewhat beyond the region of primary growth. The second is accomplished in the case of hair by having the base of the follicle well below the skin surface, so that cells displaced from the focus of active growth are still accessible to materials diffusing from adjoining parts of the skin.

The geometry of hair growth is such that cells of the main mass are elongated in the direction of displacement, giving rise to relatively well-aligned fiber bundles parallel to the direction of displacement. Components of relatively low molecular weight and high sulfur content diffuse into the fiber from the side. They interact strongly with the fiber-forming material, but are not completely miscible, forming a separate phase. Parts of the follicle most accessible to these high sulfur components are most quickly affected by them. As a result their fibrous phases are relatively poorly ordered and in lower concentration. Thus it is possible to rationalize or predict successively higher degrees of order and decreasing sulfur contents in going from the root sheath to the cuticle and then the cortex, of which the para segment is the better ordered.

Since the detailed fine structure of feather keratin is less known, its place in such a scheme is more speculative. The evidence suggests that the feather components are more compatible or homogeneous and of relatively low molecular weight. As a result, phase separation is less apparent, molecular ordering is often very extensive and well detailed, and characteristic interaction through hydrogen bonding between different polypeptide chain segments occurs extensively.

Trends and Problems in Structural Research

This discussion of keratins is necessarily limited in scope. It is intended primarily as an introduction to this important group of fibrous proteins. We have given most attention to animal hairs, these having received the most detailed study in the past. No attempt has been made to review the many contributions to keratin structure coming from studies of mechanical properties and of the penetration and diffusion into keratins of ions, dyes, and neutral molecules, including water. Also left out of this discussion are contributions from studies of the electron paramagnetic and nuclear magnetic resonance spectra of keratins, and studies of absorption of ultraviolet and infrared radiation.

But despite the wide research interest in the structure of keratins, their structure is still incompletely resolved. Aside from need to account for details of their x-ray patterns, one of the more challenging puzzles that still remain to be solved is the exact nature of the α-β transformation. For example, how do the side chains readjust themselves during extension? Perhaps new aspects of keratin structure may be clarified by study of keratins which have received little research attention up to now. There is ample opportunity for electron microscopy to assist in developing further knowledge of keratin structure, for example, by determining details of development of structure during natural keratin formation, including the resolution of subfibril components. With improved techniques, electron microscopy may conclusively establish details of the internal structure of the microfibrils and the matrix, and their relations to other cell components, such as keratohyaline granules. There is need for more information on the structure of the cell membranes. Electron microscopy will also help in showing the nature, through structure, of fragments obtained by various degradative procedures: hydrolytic, oxidative, enzymatic, and mechanical. This will be invaluable in defining the progress of chemical or physical attack on specific structural components. An unexplored but promising line of structural research is the use of electron microscopy to determine the location and structure of polymer deposits formed within the keratin mass. Electron microscopy will also help in determining the structure of keratin proteins reprecipitated or eventually recrystallized under controlled experimental conditions.

Finally, there is the important area of interpreting abnormal keratins formed in disease. What are the effects of disease on keratin structure? When we understand normal keratins and their generation we will be able to understand better the abnormalities, including cancerous cells. Keratin-forming tissue provides an excellent medium for study of protein synthesis, its specialization and deviations.

Acknowledgments

The authors are gratefully indebted to Dr. Francis T. Jones of this laboratory for preparing many photographs with the optical microscope, to Pierre Kassenbeck, Director of the Physical Laboratory, Institut Textile de France, for diagrams and discussion of scale structure and its significance, and especially to Dr. George E. Rogers, Wool Research Laboratories, C.S.I.R.O., and Dr. Jan Sikorski, Textile Physics Laboratory, University of Leeds, for illustrative material, including original electron micrographs. We also thank our colleagues, Dale R. Black, Dr. Kenneth J. Palmer, and Dr. Richard S. Thomas for critical reviews of preliminary drafts.

References

1. Mahal, G. S., Johnston, A., and Burns, R. H., *Textile Research J.* **21**, 83 (1951).
2. Swerdlow, M., and Seeman, G. S., *J. Research Natl. Bur. Standards* **41**, 231 (1948).
3. Montagna, W., and Ellis, R. A., eds., "The Biology of Hair Growth." Academic Press, New York, 1958.
4. Mercer, E. H., *in* "The Biology of Hair Growth" (W. Montagna and R. A. Ellis, eds.), Chapters 5 and 6. Academic Press, New York, 1958.
5. Rogers, G. E., *Ann. N. Y. Acad. Sci.* **83**, 378 (1959).
6. Brody, I., *J. Ultrastructure Research* **4**, 264 (1960).
7. Fraser, R. D. B., MacRae, T. P., and Rogers, G. E. *Nature* **193**, 1052 (1962).

8. Fraser, R. D. B., MacRae, T. P., and Rogers, G. E., *J. Textile Inst.* **51**, T497 (1960).
9. Sikorski, J., and Woods, H. J., *J. Textile Inst.* **51**, T506 (1960).
10. Rudall, K. M., *Biochim. et Biophys. Acta* **1**, 549 (1947).
11. Astbury, W. T., and Woods, H. J., *Phil. Trans. Roy. Soc. London* **A232**, 333 (1933).
12. Brill, R., *Ann.* **434**, 204 (1923).
13. Meyer, K. H., and Mark, H., *Ber.* **61**, 1932 (1928).
14. Bailey, K., Astbury, W. T., and Rudall, K. M., *Nature* **151**, 716 (1943).
15. Astbury, W. T., *Advances in Enzymol.* **3**, 63 (1943).
16. Astbury, W. T., *Brit. J. Dermatol. Syphilis* **62**, 1 (1950).
17. Müting, D., Langhof, H., and Wortmann, V., *Z. klin. Med.* **152**, 495 (1955).
18. Simmonds, D. H., *Australian J. Biol. Sci.* **8**, 537 (1955).
19. Fraser, R. D. B., MacRae, T. P., and Simmonds, D. H., *Biochim. et Biophys. Acta* **25**, 654 (1957).
20. Schroeder, W. A., Kay, L. M., Lewis, B., and Munger, N., *J. Am. Chem. Soc.* **77**, 3901 (1955).
21. Glauert, A. M., Rogers, G. E., and Glauert, R., *Nature* **178**, 803 (1955).
22. Kassenbeck, P., *in* "Structure de la Laine, Textes et Discussions du Colloque July 1961," p. 51. Institute Textile de France, Paris.
23. Filshie, B. K., and Rogers, G. E., *J. Mol. Biol.* **3**, 784 (1961).
24. Gillespie, J. M., *Australian J. Biol. Sci.* **13**, 81 (1960).
25. Trotman, S. R., Trotman, E. R., and Sutton, R. W., *J. Soc. Chem. Ind.* **45T**, 20 (1926).
26. Goddard, D. R., and Michaelis, L., *J. Biol. Chem.* **112**, 361 (1935).
27. Lindley, H., *Nature* **160**, 190 (1947).
28. Alexander, P., and Earland, C., *Nature* **166**, 396 (1950).
29. Speakman, J. B., and Das, D. B., *J. Soc. Dyers Colourists* **66**, 583 (1950).
30. Gillespie, J. M., and Lennox, F. G., *Biochim. et Biophys. Acta* **12**, 481 (1953).
31. Gillespie, J. M., *Biochim. et Biophys. Acta* **27**, 225 (1958).
32. Ward, W. H., and Bartulovich, J. J., *J. Phys. Chem.* **60**, 1208 (1956).
33. Corfield, M. C., Robson, A., and Skinner, B., *Biochem. J.* **68**, 348 (1958).
34. Rogers, G. E., *J. Ultrastructure Research* **2**, 309 (1959).
35. O'Donnell, I. J., and Thompson, E. O. P., *Australian J. Biol. Sci.* **12**, 294 (1959).
36. Bartulovich, J. J., Tomimatsu, Y., and Ward, W. H., *J. Textile Inst.* **51**, T628 (1960).
37. Crewther, W. G., and Dowling, L. M., *J. Textile Inst.* **51**, T775 (1960).
38. Gillespie, J. M., O'Donnell, I. J., Thompson, E. O. P., and Woods, E. F., *J. Textile Inst.* **51**, T703 (1960).
39. Rogers, G. E., *Ann. N. Y. Acad. Sci.* **83**, 408 (1959).
40. Montagna, W., "The Structure and Function of Skin." Academic Press, New York, 1956.

41. Matoltsy, A. G., in "The Biology of Hair Growth" (W. Montagna and R. A. Ellis, eds.), Chapter 7. Academic Press, New York, 1958.
42. Swanbeck, G., J. Ultrastructure Research 3, 51 (1959).
43. Swanbeck, G., Acta Dermato-Venereol. 39, Suppl. 43 (1959).
44. Anon., Wool Sci. Rev. No. 4, 35 (1949).
45. MacArthur, I., Nature 152, 38 (1943).
46. Astbury, W. T., J. Textile Sci. 4, 1 (1931).
47. Speakman, J. B., J. Soc. Dyers Colourists 52, 335 (1936).
48. von Nathusius-Königsborn, W., "Das Wollhaar des Schafes." Wiegandt, Berlin, 1866.
49. McMurtrie, W., "Examination of Wools and Other Animal Fibers." Government Printing Office, Washington, D. C., 1886.
50. Hock, C. W., Ramsay, R. C., and Harris, M., J. Research Natl. Bur. Standards 27, 181 (1941).
51. von Bergen, W., and Mauersberger, H. R., "The American Wool Handbook," 2nd ed. Textile Book, New York, 1948.
52. Reumuth, H., Melliand Textilber. 23, 1 (1942).
53. Reumuth, H., Melliand Textilber. 23, 53 (1942).
54. Reumuth, H., Klepzig's Textil-Z. 45, 149 (1942).
55. Reumuth, H., Klepzig's Textil-Z. 45, 288 (1942).
56. Auber, L., Trans. Roy. Soc. Edinburgh 62, 191 (1950-51).
57. Wildman, A. B., "The Microscopy of Animal Textile Fibres." Wool Industries Research Association, Leeds, 1954.
58. von Bergen, W., and Krauss, W., "Textile Fiber Atlas." Textile Book, New York, 1949.
59. Harris, M., "Handbook of Textile Fibers." Interscience, New York, and Harris Research Laboratories, Washington, D. C., 1954.
60. Kassenbeck, P., Personal communication.
61. Dobb, M. G., Johnston, F. R., Nott, J. A., Oster, L., Sikorski, J., and Simpson, W. S., J. Textile Inst. 52, T153 (1961).
62. Ohara, K., Melliand Textilber. 19, 407 (1938).
63. Horio, M., and Kondo, T., Textile Research J. 23, 373 (1953).
64. Mercer, E. H., Textile Research J., 23, 388 (1953).
65. Mercer, E. H., Textile Research J. 24, 39 (1954).
66. Rudall, K. M., Proc. Intern. Wool Textile Research Conf., Australia, F9 (1955).
67. Durward, A., and Rudall, K. M., Proc. Intern. Wool Textile Research Conf., Australia, F112 (1955).
68. Mercer, E. H., Farrant, J. L., and Rees, A. L. G., Proc. Intern. Wool Textile Research Conf., Australia, F120 (1955).
69. Dusenbury, J. H., and Menkart, J., Proc. Intern. Wool Textile Research Conf., Australia, F142 (1955).
70. Fraser, R. D. B., and Rogers, G. E., Proc. Intern. Wool Textile Research Conf., Australia, F151 (1955).
71. Leveau, M., Bull. inst. textile France No. 74, 75 (1958).
72. Kassenbeck, P., Bull. inst. textile France No. 83, 25 (1959).
73. Kassenbeck, P., Ing. textil 26, 462 (1960).

74. Wildman, A. B., *Proc. Intern. Wool Textile Research Conf., Australia,* **F156** (1955).
75. Lindberg, J., Mercer, E. H., Philip, B., and Gralén, N., *Textile Research J.* **19**, 673 (1949).
76. Ramanathan, N., Sikorski, J., and Woods, H. J., *Biochim. et Biophys. Acta* **18**, 323 (1955).
77. Lindberg, J., Philip, B., and Gralén, N., *Nature* **162**, 458 (1948).
78. Lindberg, J., *Textile Research J.* **19**, 43 (1949).
79. Lagermalm, G., *Textile Research J.* **24**, 17 (1954).
80. Fraser, R. D. B., and Rogers, G. E., *Australian J. Biol. Sci.* **8**, 129 (1955).
81. Fraser, R. D. B., and Rogers, G. E., *Biochim. et Biophys. Acta* **16**, 307 (1955).
82. Birbeck, M. S. C., and Mercer, E. H., *J. Biophys. Biochem. Cytol.* **3**, 215 (1957).
83. Gorter, C. J., and Houwink, A. L., *Proc. Koninkl. Ned. Akad. Wetenschap.* **51**, 262 (1948); *Vezelinst. T.N.O., Mededel.* **89** (1948).
84. Bekker, J. G., and King, A. T., *Biochem. J.* **25**, 1077 (1931).
85. Matoltsy, A. G., *Exptl. Cell Research* **5**, 98 (1953).
86. Rogers, G. E., and Rowlands, to be published, cited in reference (39).
87. Blackburn, S., *Biochem. J.* **43**, 114 (1948).
88. Rudall, K. M., *Proc. Intern. Wool Textile Research Conf., Australia,* **F176** (1955).
89. Zahn, H., *Melliand Textilber.* **21**, 505 (1940).
90. Zahn, H., *Melliand Textilber.* **22**, 305 (1941).
91. Zahn, H., *Melliand Textilber.* **23**, 157 (1942).
92. Zahn, H., *Melliand Textilber.* **24**, 157 (1943).
93. Hock, C. W., and McMurdie, H. F., *J. Research Natl. Bur. Standards* **31**, 229 (1943).
94. Mercer, E. H., and Rees, A. L. G., *Nature* **157**, 589 (1946).
95. Mercer, E. H., and Rees, A. L. G., *Australian J. Exptl. Biol. Med. Sci.* **24**, 147 (1946).
96. Mercer, E. H., and Rees, A. L. G., *Australian J. Exptl. Biol. Med. Sci.* **24**, 175 (1946).
97. Farrant, J. L., Rees, A. L. G., and Mercer, E. H., *Nature* **159**, 535 (1947).
98. Olofsson, B., *Medd. Svenska Textilforskningsinst. Göteborg* **2**, 3 (1946).
99. Philip, B., and Lagermalm, G., *in* "Proceedings of the Conference on Electron Microscopy, Delft, July 1949," p. 166. Nijhoff, The Hague, 1950.
100. Lagermalm, G., and Philip, B., *Textile Research J.* **20**, 668 (1950).
101. Lagermalm, G., *Medd. Svenska Textilforskninginst. Göteborg* **14**, 65 (1951).
102. Barnes, R. B., Burton, C. J., and Scott, R. G., *J. Appl. Phys.* **16**, 730 (1945).
103. Kern, S. F., *J. Polymer Sci.* **1**, 259 (1946).
104. Makinson, K. R., *Textile Research J.* **20**, 22 (1950).
105. Birbeck, M. S. C., and Mercer, E. H., *in* "Electron Microscopy, Proceed-

ings of The Stockholm Conference, Sept. 1956" (F. S. Sjöstrand and J. Rhodin, eds.), p. 156. Academic Press, New York, 1957.

106. Birbeck, M. S. C., and Mercer, E. H., *in* "Electron Microscopy, Proceedings of The Stockholm Conference, Sept. 1956" (F. S. Sjöstrand and J. Rhodin, eds.), p. 158. Academic Press, New York, 1957.

107. Birbeck, M. S. C., and Mercer, E. H., *J. Biophys. Biochem. Cytol.* **3**, 203 (1957).

108. Birbeck, M. S. C., and Mercer, E. H., *J. Biophys. Biochem. Cytol.* **3**, 223 (1957).

109. Birbeck, M. S. C., Mercer, E. H., and Barnicot, N. A., *Exptl. Cell Research* **10**, 505 (1956).

110. Elliott, R. L., and Manogue, B., *J. Soc. Dyers Colourists* **68**, 12 (1952).

111. Manogue, B., and Elliott, R. L., *J. Soc. Dyers Colourists* **69**, 113 (1953).

112. Manogue, B., Moss, M. S., and Elliott, R. L., *J. Soc. Dyers Colourists* **70**, 502 (1954).

113. Jeffrey, G. M., Sikorski, J., and Woods, H. J., *Textile Research J.* **25**, 714 (1955).

114. Jeffrey, G. M., Sikorski, J., and Woods, H. J., *Proc. Intern. Wool Textile Research Conf., Australia,* **F130** (1955).

115. Ramanathan, N., Sikorski, J., and Woods, H. J., *Proc. Intern. Wool Textile Research Conf., Australia,* **F92** (1955).

116. Sikorski, J., and Simpson, W. S., *Nature* **182**, 1235 (1958).

117. Laxer, G., Sikorski, J., Whewell, C. S., and Woods, H. J., *Biochim. et Biophys. Acta* **15**, 174 (1954).

118. Lyne, A. G., and Heidman, M. J., *Australian J. Biol. Sci.* **12**, 72 (1959).

119. Galtsoff, P. S., and Philpott, D. E., *J. Ultrastructure Research* **3**, 241 (1960).

120. Alexander, P., and Hudson, R. F., "Wool, Its Chemistry and Physics." Reinhold, New York, 1954.

121. Gillespie, J. M., *Biochim. et Biophys. Acta* **27**, 225 (1958).

122. Fraser, R. D. B., and MacRae, T. P., *Nature* **179**, 732 (1957).

123. Bear, R. S., and Rugo, H. J., *Ann. N. Y. Acad. Sci.* **53**, 627 (1951).

124. Astbury, W. T., and Sisson, W. A., *Proc. Roy. Soc. (London)* **A150**, 533 (1935).

125. Corey, R. B., and Wyckoff, R. W. G., *J. Biol. Chem.* **114**, 407 (1936).

126. Peacock, N., *Biochim. et Biophys. Acta* **32**, 220 (1959).

127. Bamford, C. H., Elliott, A., and Hanby, W. E., "Synthetic Polypeptides." Academic Press, New York, 1956.

128. Bradbury, E. M., Brown, L., Downie, A. R., Elliott, A., Fraser, R. D. B., Hanby, W. E., and McDonald, T. R. R., *J. Mol. Biol.* **2**, 276 (1960).

129. Pauling, L., and Corey, R. B., *J. Am. Chem. Soc.* **72**, 5349 (1950).

130. Pauling, L., Corey, R. B., and Branson, H. R., *Proc. Natl. Acad. Sci. U. S.* **37**, 205 (1951).

131. Pauling, L., and Corey, R. B., *Proc. Natl. Acad. Sci. U. S.* **37**, 235 (1951).

132. Low, B. W., *in* "The Proteins" (H. Neurath and K. Bailey, eds.), Vol. I, Part A, Chapter 4. Academic Press, New York, 1954.

133. Crick, F. H. C., *Nature* **170**, 882 (1952).

134. Crick, F. H. C., *Acta Cryst.* **6**, 689 (1953).
135. Pauling, L., and Corey, R. B., *Nature* **171**, 59 (1953).
136. Fraser, R. D. B., and MacRae, T. P., *Textile Research J.* **27**, 384 (1957).
137. Fraser, R. D. B., and MacRae, T. P., *Biochim. et Biophys. Acta* **29**, 229 (1958).
138. Swanbeck, G., *Exptl. Cell Research* **23**, 420 (1961).
139. Huggins, M. L., *Proc. Natl. Acad. Sci. U. S.* **43**, 204 (1957).
140. Huggins, M. L., "Physical Chemistry of High Polymers." Wiley, New York, 1958.
141. Huggins, M. L., *J. Polymer Sci.* **50**, 65 (1961).
142. Fraser, R. D. B., and MacRae, T. P., *Nature* **189**, 572 (1961).
143. Fraser, R. D. B., and MacRae, T. P., *J. Mol. Biol.* **3**, 640 (1961).
144. Thompson, E. O. P., *Austral. J. Biol. Sci.* **12**, 303 (1959).
145. Lillie, F. R., *Biol. Revs.* **17**, 247 (1942).
146. Fox, D. L., "Animal Biochromes and Structural Colours." Cambridge Univ. Press, London and New York, 1953.
147. Storer, T. I., "General Zoology." McGraw-Hill, New York, 1951.
148. Frank, F., and Ruska, H., *Naturwissenschaften* **27**, 229 (1939).
149. Ward, W. H., Binkley, C. H., and Snell, N. S., *Textile Research J.* **25**, 314 (1955).
150. Auber, L., and Appleyard, H. M., *Nature* **168**, 736 (1951).
151. Philip, B., Lagermalm, G., and Gralén, N., *Biochim. et Biophys. Acta* **6**, 497 (1951).
152. Schor, R., and Krimm, S., *Biophys. J.* **1**, 467 (1961).
153. Pauling, L., and Corey, R. B., *Proc. Natl. Acad. Sci. U. S.* **37**, 729 (1951).
154. Astbury, W. T., and Beighton, E., *Nature* **191**, 171 (1961).
155. Fraser, R. D. B., and MacRae, T. P., *J. Mol. Biol.* **1**, 387 (1959).
156. Schor, R., and Krimm, S., *Biophys. J.* **1**, 489 (1961).
157. Woodin, A. M., *Biochem. J.* **57**, 99 (1954).
158. Corey, R. B., and Pauling, L., *Proc. Intern. Wool Textile Research Conf., Australia*, **B249** (1955).

Some Aspects of the Ultrastructure of α-Keratin, Bacterial Flagella, and Feather Keratin

G. E. ROGERS AND B. K. FILSHIE

Division of Protein Chemistry, Wool Research Laboratories,
C.S.I.R.O., Melbourne, Australia

Studies with the electron microscope have produced considerable advances in our knowledge of the macromolecular architecture of fibrous proteins especially as a result of continued refinements in technique. Investigations of α-keratins have not led to conclusions as far-reaching as in the case of muscle or collagen, for example; nevertheless, information on microfibrillar organization has already been obtained for this group and usefully correlated with chemical and x-ray diffraction data (1–8).

One of the more recently recognized members of the keratin-myosin-epidermin-fibrinogen (KMEF) group of proteins is that of bacterial flagella which have been studied by Weibull (9) and Astbury and Weibull (10). Bacterial flagella are protein in nature and yield an x-ray diffraction pattern of the α type with reflections closely allied to those given by α-keratin, and consequently have been likened to macromolecular "hairs" (11). Subfibrils which might exist in these structures, equivalent to the subfibrils of the larger animal flagella have not been detected by electron microscopy in the flagella from *Proteus vulgaris* and *Bacillus subtilis* used for x-ray studies by Astbury and co-workers. There is convincing evidence that the flagella of some species consist of 2 or 3 subfibrils wound around each other in the form of left-handed or right-handed helices (12–14).

Feather keratin is a further fibrous protein which has been subjected to detailed analysis by the x-ray diffraction technique, leading to the formulation of a number of possible structural models (15–21). Feather keratin is of interest because of its histological and chemical relationships to α-keratin, and also because of the similarity of its x-ray pattern to the β pattern produced when α-keratin is stretched to extensions up to 100%, suggesting that there are features common to both in the underlying molecular organization. However, information on the fine structure of feather keratin from electron microscopy has been lacking.

The present discussion is concerned therefore with fine structural details which have recently been observed with the electron microscope and which give some further insight into the macromolecular organization in all three of these different fibrous proteins.

α-Keratin. α-Keratins whether of wool, hair, porcupine quill, nail, horn or the keratinized surface layers of the epidermis consist of microfibrils about 80 Å in diameter embedded in a matrix of apparently amorphous protein. This matrix contains a significantly higher proportion of the amino acids cystine, proline, serine, and threonine than the microfibrillar protein (2–4). The microfibrils are believed to consist of protein chains which are arranged in a more orderly fashion than those in the matrix (5–7).

In order to examine the "microfibril + matrix" complex of an α-keratin by electron microscopy, it is first necessary to treat the material with a reducing agent such as thioglycolic acid (TGA) and then to subsequently treat the partially reduced α-keratin with osmium tetroxide (OsO_4) (TGA-OsO_4 procedure). The keratin turns black rapidly as the OsO_4 is reduced by the SH groups. The stained keratin is embedded in Araldite (22, 23) for ultrathin

---

FIG. 1. Cross section of part of the cortex of a wool fiber (Australian Merino 90's) taken where cells meet at the junction between the paracortex (P) and the orthocortex (O). Several paracortical cells can be seen to have been sectioned at varying levels and are much denser than those of the orthocortex owing to the amount of densely staining matrix present between the microfibrils in this segment. There are regions where there is an accumulation of matrix (m) and no microfibrils. In other cells the microfibrils (mf) with their matrix are packed together in a variety of arrays. In comparison, it is difficult to distinguish the "microfibrils + matrix" in the orthocortex. In this segment "microfibrils + matrix" occur in roughly circular "packets" or macrofibrils. The cell membrane complex (cm) can be distinguished, and in the paracortex the cell boundaries appear to have contracted away from the band of intercellular cementing material. TGA-OsO_4 method, section stained with lead hydroxide.

sectioning. It was found that without prior reduction of the keratin, OsO_4 reacts weakly but predominantly with the matrix material, thereby enabling the microfibrils to be vaguely outlined in the electron microscope. However, the initial partial reduction step leads to a much more extensive reaction with OsO_4 and consequently a clearer delineation of the microfibrils and matrix by virtue of the increased contrast (3).

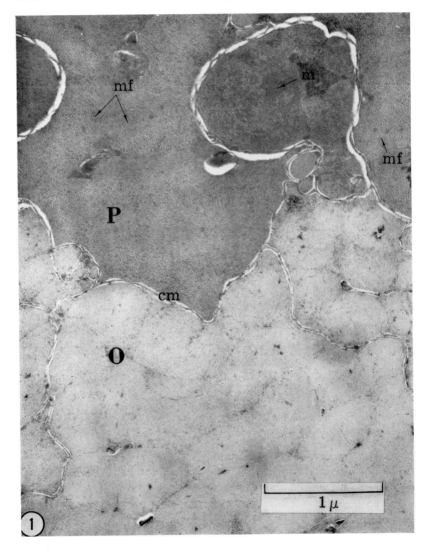

Recently it has been found (24) that a further improvement in contrast can be achieved by further staining the sections of reduced and OsO_4-treated keratins with solutions of lead salts or lead hydroxide (25). The application of these methods of "electron staining" and Araldite embedding has made possible the surveying of the ways in which microfibrils pack together in the matrix material in different α-keratins (2, 3, 25a). Wide variations have been found and some arrangements are more characteristic of particular α-keratins. A striking example is shown in Fig. 1 which is a portion of the cortex of a fine Australian Merino wool fiber in cross section. The fibers of this type of wool are highly crimped or curly, a characteristic originating in the cortex which is bilaterally asymmetric with respect to a number of physical and chemical properties (26). Moreover, marked differences in the component cortical cells on the two sides of the fiber can be readily recognized in the fine structural details visible in the electron micrograph. In the cortical cells of the segment of the fiber called the paracortex, microfibrils are clearly visible with the electron-dense matrix material located around and between them. In addition, it can be seen that the amount of matrix is variable in different regions of the paracortex but clearly this component is more abundant than in the keratin of the cells of the orthocortex, the other segment of the fiber. It is found, too, that individual microfibrils are frequently outlined in paracortical cells, and their organization ranges from near-perfect hexagonal packing to totally irregular close-packing. In orthocortical cells there is a lower ratio of matrix to microfibrils, and the microfibrils are arrayed in the form of circular sheets or lamellae with individual microfibrils usually visible only in the center of the formation, the total structure being termed a macrofibril. These two major organizational features of "paracortical-type" and "orthocortical-type" are illustrated in more detail in Figs. 2 and 3,

---

FIG. 2.   A higher magnification view of an array of "microfibrils + matrix" in a cross section of a paracortical cell. The protofibrillar substructure in the microfibrils can be clearly seen. TGA-OsO_4 method, section stained with lead hydroxide.

FIG. 3.   As in Fig. 2, but an orthocortical cell. Portions of two macrofibrils are present, with the centrally placed microfibrils clearly delineated, whereas further out the microfibrils are arrayed in cylindrical laminae, with denser-staining matrix between the layers. TGA-OsO_4 method, section stained with lead hydroxide.

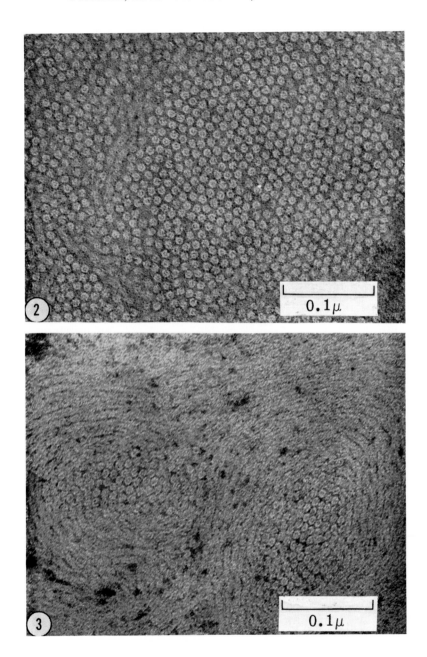

and it is found that both of these occur to different extents and with some modification in all α-keratinous structures.

A most important recent finding is the presence of substructure within microfibrils of all α-keratins so far examined (24) which only becomes visible in the electron microscope after staining with lead salts or lead hydroxide. In Figs. 2 and 3 it can already be seen that a high concentration of lead has entered each microfibril and is bound to preferred sites, revealing a composite structure consisting of filamentous subunits relatively unstained by lead, called protofibrils, each of the order of 20 Å in diameter. These protofibrils are arrayed peripherally around a stained central region containing an unstained core. The total arrangement bears a strong resemblance to that of subfibrils of animal flagella in which the occurrence of the basic "9 + 2" organization of subfibrils is well established (27–29) and may also extend to bacterial flagella as well (11). The substructure in the keratin microfibrils is shown in Fig. 4 at higher magnification and presented as a "negative" print. Although it is not possible at present to establish the exact number of protofibrils per microfibril, it appears to be close to "9 + 2" and this was more convincing when repetitive prints were made from different microfibrils showing the best delineation of structure (Fig. 4a).

The component α-helices of a microfibril therefore are not arranged in a close-packed manner but are organized into protofibrils, and it is highly probable that each protofibril is a compound helix of the coiled-coil type already suggested for α-keratin (16, 30). Furthermore, it is reasonable to assume that there are several protein chains filling the space between the protofibrils. It is into this interstitial region that the lead penetrates, whereas the organized chains of the protofibrils would be expected to be inaccessible.

Fraser and MacRae (31) have tested the 3-strand rope structure (triple helix) of Crick, using an optical diffractometer. They found a close agreement between the optical transforms of this and similar structures and the observed x-ray diagram of α-keratin, especially in the case where the deformation necessary for coiling was restricted to specific points rather than being continuous as in Crick's structure. Moreover, they have performed some tests of the "9 + 2" model (unpublished work) by obtaining optical transforms from arbitrary settings of the relative arrangements of the protofibrils (each equivalent to a triple helix) in neighboring microfibrils.

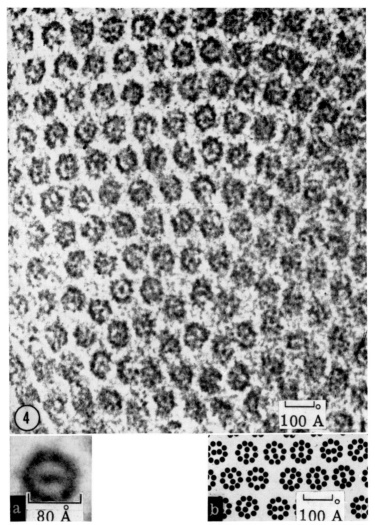

FIG. 4.   Cross section of part of the paracortex of a wool fiber showing the protofibrillar constitution of individual microfibrils. Each microfibril appears to consist of a peripheral array of ∼20-Å protofibrils surrounding a core of protofibrils. The delineation of this substructure is highly imperfect, but the likelihood of a "9 + 2" flagella type of pattern was more convincingly illustrated when a multiple print was prepared from a number of microfibril images showing this substructure, in an attempt to reduce the background "noise" (Fig. 4a). An idealized interpretation of the postulated structure is given in Fig. 4b. From a section of wool treated by TGA-OsO$_4$ and section stained with lead hydroxide.

They found that the model yielded results compatible with the observed x-ray diagram.

Since flagella give α-type x-ray patterns and thus share structural features as well as contractile properties with the KMEF group, it is of profound significance for the elucidation of the structure of α-keratin to have direct evidence of a macromolecular organization which is common to both α-keratin and animal flagella. More recent electron microscope studies, however, indicate the unlikelihood of the "9 + 2" subfibrillar organization being shared by bacterial flagella, and this evidence will now be discussed.

Bacterial Flagella. Peritrichous flagella of bacteria such as *Proteus vulgaris* can be detached from the cell bodies by mechanical agitation and isolated in quantities (9) sufficient for characterization by chemical and biophysical techniques (9, 11, 32–34). Such isolated flagella have been examined with the electron microscope by Rogers and Filshie (35). By negative staining (36) of freshly prepared flagella, and comparison in the same field with tobacco mosaic virus rods which measure 150 Å in diameter, it was established that the flagella diameter was close to the usually reported value of 120 Å obtained from shadowed specimens. The flagella appeared to almost completely resist a selective uptake of heavy metals such as to reveal any substructure which might be contained within, despite many experiments in which pH and composition [phosphotungstic acid (PTA), uranyl acetate, phosphomolybdic acid] of the negative stain were varied.

However in many PTA-stained preparations short particles about 600 Å long and 150 Å wide were found either free, or attached to one end of a flagellum (see Fig. 5). These entities are the "rootlets" or bases of the flagella which have been described before as "hooks"

Fig. 5. Bacterial flagella (*Proteus vulgaris*) preparation negatively stained with PTA, pH 5.6. The field chosen shows a relatively high concentration of "rootlets" (r) which have broken off from flagella, although in one instance a "rootlet" remains attached to its flagellum (Fr). The "rootlets" show some fine structure as yet uninterpreted but possibly a helix of particulate subunits, and in the two flagella (F_1, F_2) some sign of the same fine structure can be seen along their lengths. Several ∼50-Å wide filaments (f) are to be seen. These are fimbriae.

Fig. 5a. Cross section of several flagella fixed with OsO_4, embedded in Araldite, and the sections stained with lead hydroxide. The flagella show a dense periphery and less-dense core.

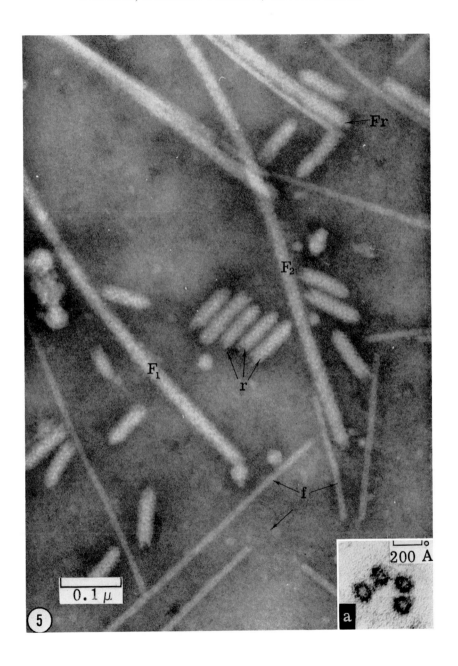

(37) and presumably come from within the bacterial body. Many remain attached to the flagella during the isolation procedure. The attachment between rootlet and flagellum is apparently weak, and so the rootlets break off as a result of the mechanical stresses which operate during the spraying of the preparations onto the electron microscope grids. They are readily distinguished from the flagella proper because they have a fine substructure in the form of an ordered array of unstained particles each some 30–40 Å in diameter arranged in such a way as to give a "woven" appearance (Fig. 5). Although the interpretation of this appearance is problematical the structure is probably some type of helical arrangement. Occasionally there are indications that the same substructure is present in the flagella themselves but attempts to reveal this structure in the flagella with greater certainty by partially degrading them with ultrasonics, detergents, proteases, changes in pH, and freezing and thawing have not been successful. On the other hand Kerridge et al. (37a) have found definite evidence of helical arrays of 45 Å diameter particles in flagella isolated from *Salmonella typhimurium*.

In addition to the flagella the negatively stained preparations show the presence of a number of finer filaments, about 50 Å in diameter (Fig. 5). These filaments are fimbriae (38, 39) which are attached to and project out from the bacterial body as do flagella, and are detached with the flagella by the shaking treatment during preparation. The fimbriae filaments are generally not as long as the flagella.

The number of fimbriae present in flagella preparations varied, but their widths were consistently less than half the diameter of a normal flagellum, that is about 50 Å. Occasionally other forms were observed which consisted of 2 or 3 fimbriae twisted together in helical form (Fig. 6) but usually fimbriae occurred singly and were relatively straight. In some electron micrographs each fimbria appeared to be composed of two finer filaments and each of the finer filaments to consist of a row of spherical particles. It cannot be stated at this stage whether fimbriae and flagella are structurally related or have macromolecular structural components in common. Nor is it known what function fimbriae play in bacterial activity. It is probable that they play no part in motility but have a function relating to the attachment of the bacteria to other cell surfaces.

It is not possible at present to describe the ultrastructure of *Proteus vulgaris* flagella in definitive terms. However, the study of ultrathin sections of flagella does not lend support to the suggestion by Astbury *et al.* (*11*) of a "9 + 2" internal structure of subfibrils in bacterial flagella. Cross sections of flagella stained with lead hydroxide show that the lead is taken up preferentially by the periphery of the flagellum leaving an unstained core (Fig. 5a). This means that if the helical arrangement of particles observed in the flagella rootlets is, in fact, the major structural arrange-

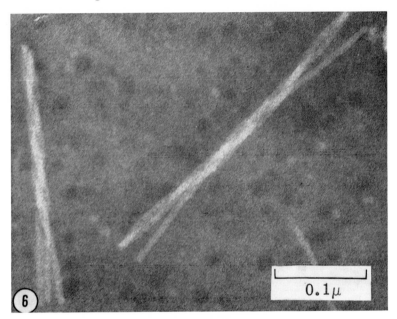

FIG. 6. Two examples of ∼50-Å wide filaments, the fimbriae. These fimbriae have aggregated together and twisted around one another. Such appearances are observed in preparations which have been negatively stained with PTA. True flagella have not been observed to behave in this manner.

ment in the flagella proper, then the helices of particles are represented either by the unstained core (and the stained periphery is a sheath of protein of another type) or by the stained periphery. There are difficulties with both interpretations but these should be resolved by further studies.

A helical structure for *Proteus* flagella would have the desirable feature of being similar to the flagella structure of several other species which have been found to be helical (*12–14*), and sheaths around flagella also have been recognized in some bacteria (*37*) and hence could be expected. A triple helix model is compatible with the available x-ray diffraction data according to the models considered by Burge (*40*).

Finally, it is appropriate to mention that the present authors' investigations have not confirmed the reported observations of Smith, Burge, and Randall (see *40*) that the use of PTA in the negative-staining method showed the presence of phosphotungstate along an axial core of the flagella and that the diameters of the flagella were increased by about 100%. In the authors' experience it is possible to find objects conforming with this description, but which are almost certainly the tail sheaths derived from bacteriophage present in the bacterial cultures and carried over into the flagella preparations.

Feather Keratin. Previous studies of feather keratin with the electron microscope have been of a preliminary kind (*41*, *42*) and have only revealed fibrous elements of macrofibril dimensions. Recently, Filshie and Rogers (*43*) examined thin sections of specimens of feather rachis which had been treated with OsO_4, but were unable to detect any evidence of fine structure, despite the fact that OsO_4 is known to intensify the low-angle equatorial x-ray reflection of 34 Å as shown by Fraser and MacRae (*17*) who concluded that osmium deposits were external to the fibrous elements. Feather rachis was treated by the TGA-OsO_4 procedure as used for α-keratins but again no fine structure was observed. However, when thin sections of this material were stained with lead hydroxide (*25*), microfibrils could be readily resolved as shown in Fig. 7. The microfibrils are of the order of 30 Å in diameter compared with 80 Å for α-keratins, and their center-center separation is approximately 35 Å. In addition to the groups of individual microfibrils, limited areas of layers can be seen with a distance between layers of about 35 Å identical with the center-center separation of individual microfibrils. The occurrence of layers apparently arises from the close aggregation of microfibrils to form sheets one microfibril thick, with the lead-stainable regions between the sheets. Although the microfibrillar organization bears an over-all resemblance to that found in α-keratins, the packing arrangements in feather are irregular compared to the rather specialized patterns found in α-keratins.

Since the ability to resolve the feather microfibrils depends upon the metal staining of a region between the microfibrils it is reasonable to assume that as in α-keratins this region consists of an amorphous protein matrix. It would appear, however, that the cystine content of the feather matrix is not greatly different from that

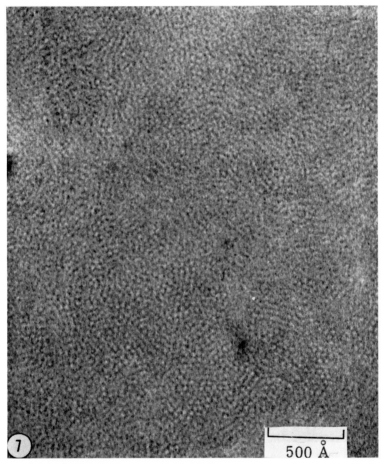

500 Å

FIG. 7. Cross section of mature feather rachis showing the "microfibril + matrix" type of constitution similar to α-keratin. The microfibrils are ~30 Å in diameter, with a center-center separation of ~35 Å. TGA-OsO$_4$ method, section stained with lead hydroxide.

of the microfibrils, because of the lack of staining by the TGA-OsO$_4$ procedure. The "microfibril + matrix" type of organization seems the most plausible one based on the evidence so far, although the selective uptake of lead could possibly be explained by a penetration and attachment of lead to the peripheral protein chains of each microfibril.

It is too early to make any detailed comments on the significance of the ~30-Å diameter feather microfibrils in relation to published x-ray studies of feather and the structural models derived from these. The prominent equatorial x-ray reflection at 34 Å almost certainly arises from the microfibrils which have a center-center separation estimated from the electron micrographs to be of the order of 35 Å. The structure for feather based on a cable of seven collagen triple helices as suggested by Ramachandran and Dweltz (19) and Dweltz (18) is a unit with a diameter comparable with that observed for the microfibril. The model suggested by Bear and Rugo (15) in which ellipsoid-shaped micelles are arranged end-to-end on a 2-dimensional lattice does not describe a 3-dimensional microfibrillar structure. However, Fraser and MacRae (unpublished observations) have examined the possibility that the microfibril is composed of a helical array of micelles of the type envisaged by Bear and Rugo. They found that the diffraction properties are compatible with the observed x-ray pattern. Finally, it is pertinent to mention that the 67-Å diameter stable aggregate proposed by Schor and Krimm (20, 21) would not be consistent with a ~30-Å diameter microfibril.

The present demonstration of a microfibrillar constitution for feather keratin should be useful in future investigations into the specific arrangements of polypeptide chains in this fibrous protein.

ACKNOWLEDGMENT

The authors wish to acknowledge discussions with Miss A. M. Glauert, Strangeways Laboratory, Cambridge, on her unpublished work concerning the structure of flagella.

REFERENCES

1. Birbeck, M. S. C., and Mercer, E. H., *J. Biophys. Biochem. Cytol.* **3**, 203 (1957).
2. Rogers, G. E., *J. Ultrastructure Research* **2**, 309 (1959).
3. Rogers, G. E., *Ann. N.Y. Acad. Sci.* **83**, 378 (1959).
4. Rogers, G. E., *Ann. N.Y. Acad. Sci.* **83**, 408 (1959).
5. Fraser, R. D. B., MacRae, T. P., and Rogers, G. E., *Nature* **183**, 592 (1959).
6. Fraser, R. D. B., MacRae, T. P., and Rogers, G. E., *J. Textile Inst.* **51**, T497 (1960).

7. Fraser, R. D. B., MacRae, T. P., and Rogers, G. E., *Nature* **193**, 1052 (1962).
8. Sikorski, J., and Woods, H. J., *J. Textile Inst.* **51**, T506 (1960).
9. Weibull, C., *Biochim. et Biophys. Acta* **2**, 351 (1948).
10. Astbury, F. T., and Weibull, C., *Nature* **163**, 280 (1949).
11. Astbury, W. T., Beighton, E., and Weibull, C., *Symposia Soc. Exptl. Biol.* **9**, 306 (1955).
12. Starr, M. P., and Williams, R. C., *J. Bacteriol.* **63**, 701 (1952).
13. Labaw, L. W., and Mosley, V. M., *Biochim. et Biophys. Acta* **15**, 325 (1954).
14. Labaw, L. W., and Mosley, V. M., *Biochim. et Biophys. Acta* **17**, 322 (1955).
15. Bear, R. S., and Rugo, H. J., *Ann. N.Y. Acad. Sci.* **53**, 627 (1951).
16. Pauling, L., and Corey, R. B., *Nature* **171**, 59 (1953).
17. Fraser, R. D. B., and MacRae, T. P., *J. Mol. Biol.* **1**, 387 (1959).
18. Dweltz, N. E., *Seminar on Collagen, Central Leather Research Inst. (C.S.I.R., India), Adyar, Madras* (1960).
19. Ramachandran, G. N., and Dweltz, N. E., *Seminar on Collagen, Central Leather Research Inst. (C.S.I.R., India), Adyar, Madras* (1960).
20. Schor, R., and Krimm, S., *Biophys. J.* **1**, 467 (1961).
21. Schor, R., and Krimm, S., *Biophys. J.* **1**, 489 (1961).
22. Glauert, A. M., Rogers, G. E., and Glauert, R. H., *Nature* **178**, 803 (1956).
23. Glauert, A. M., and Glauert, R. H., *J. Biophys. Biochem. Cytol.* **4**, 191 (1958).
24. Filshie, B. K., and Rogers, G. E., *J. Mol. Biol.* **3**, 784 (1961).
25. Watson, M. L., *J. Biophys. Biochem. Cytol.* **4**, 727 (1958).
25a. Rogers, G. E., and Filshie, B. K., to be submitted to *J. Ultrastructure Research* (1963).
26. Fraser, R. D. B., and Rogers, G. E., *Australian J. Biol. Sci.* **8**, 288 (1955).
27. Bradfield, J. R. G., *Symposia Soc. Exptl. Biol.* **9**, 306 (1955).
28. Afzelius, B., *J. Biophys. Biochem. Cytol.* **5**, 269 (1959).
29. Gibbons, I. R., and Grimstone, A. V., *J. Biophys. Biochem. Cytol.* **7**, 697 (1960).
30. Crick, F. H. C., *Acta Cryst.* **6**, 689 (1953).
31. Fraser, R. D. B., and MacRae, T. P., *J. Mol. Biol.* **3**, 640 (1961).
32. Weibull, C., *Biochim. et Biophys. Acta* **3**, 378 (1949).
33. Weibull, C., *Acta Chem. Scand.* **7**, 335 (1953).
34. Kobayashi, T., Rinker, J. N., and Koffler, H., *Arch. Biochem. Biophys.* **84**, 342 (1959).
35. Rogers, G. E., and Filshie, B. K., to be submitted to *Exptl. Cell Research* (1963).
36. Brenner, S., and Horne, R. W., *Biochim. et Biophys. Acta* **34**, 103 (1959).
37. Van Iterson, W., *Intern. Congr. Microbiol., 6th Congr., Rome*, Symposium I: Bacterial Cytol., p. 24 (1953).
37a. Kerridge, D., Horne, R. W., and Glauert, A. M., *J. Mol. Biol.* **4**, 227 (1962).

38. Duguid, J. P., Smith, I. W., Dempster, G., and Edmunds, P. N., *J. Pathol. Bacteriol.* **70**, 335 (1955).
39. Duguid, J. P., and Gillies, R. R., *J. Pathol. Bacteriol.* **74**, 397 (1957).
40. Burge, R. E., *Proc. Roy. Soc.* **260A**, 558 (1960).
41. Mercer, E. H., *in* "Biology of Hair Growth" (W. Montagna and R. A. Ellis, eds.), p. 91. Academic Press, New York, 1958.
42. Sikorski, J., private communication (1961).
43. Filshie, B. K., and Rogers, G. E., *J. Cell. Biol.* **13**, 1 (1962).

Fibrous Protein Systems in Muscle

William H. Johnson[*]

Department of Physiology, University of Illinois, Urbana, Illinois

It would indeed be an understatement to say that the study of the ultrastructure of muscles using electron microscopic techniques has altered our concept of the organization of fibrous proteins within the muscle cell. Such studies have also led to an entirely new concept of how such proteins might interact to produce the phenomena associated with contraction. This is not only true in the case of the vertebrate skeletal muscles, but is also true of those muscles which had been previously classed together as smooth muscles. As the result of recent electron microscopic findings, the classification of muscles of the latter type must be completely revised. The term "smooth muscle" represents, in reality, a stage of ignorance in the quest for further refinement of muscle structure. The same is certainly true of the many cases in cytology where use of the electron microscope has filled up spaces within cells which, in the light microscope, had previously appeared to be optically empty.

A great deal was known about the fibrous proteins of muscle before what might be designated as the structural revolution occurred. Such knowledge of the physical properties, dimensions, and biochemical behavior of these proteins gave rise to numerous attempts to explain muscle contraction in terms of molecular events occurring in what was then thought to be essentially a matrix of high polymer molecules. Each molecule, or molecular complex, was thought to participate in the contractile process by undergoing a change in configuration due to changes in molecular charge (*1*),

---

[*] Present address: Department of Biology, Rensselaer Polytechnic Institute, Troy, New York.

melting out of microcrystalline regions (2), or folding of the molecule owing to entropy changes following reduction of forces which tended to hold the molecule extended (3, 4; for review, see 5). For our discussion, the important point is that in all of these models for contraction, the sarcomere of cross-striated muscle was considered to be a cross-linked polymeric system which could shorten preferentially in the axial direction and thus lift a weight or develop tension. The above molecular configurational changes were grossly expressed as mechanical work of the type performed by muscles because the working molecules were axially oriented within the matrix, but the system was in essence thought to be a polymer system similar to polymethacrylic acid or the like.

Oriented polyelectrolyte systems of nonbiological organic polymers can be made to perform mechanical work at the expense of chemical reactions, such as neutralization of acids or bases; this has been amply demonstrated by Kuhn (6) and Katchalsky (7) on cross-linked polyacrylic acid–polyvinyl alcohol systems and on others. Extensive calculations have been done on model systems to show that the fibrous proteins of muscle could behave in this way, given conditions quite similar to those which might be present in the muscle cell (8). These systems were also shown to be feasible from a thermodynamic point of view (8). There is indeed something esthetically pleasing about such systems, for, according to these systems, the events occurring during muscle contraction could be attributed to molecular events which could be understood in terms of the behavior of organic polymers. Thus much of the work which has been done on the physical chemistry of such polymeric systems could be used in the attempt to understand the contractile process.

However, during the past decade, use of the electron microscope coupled with both x-ray analysis and biochemical extraction of muscles has led to what is essentially a morphological picture of the contractile process (reviewed in 9, 10). Out of this work has grown a theory of contraction known as the sliding filament theory, a hypothesis which is well documented and thus need not be described in any detail here. According to this theory, one set of filaments ($\sim$50 Å in diameter) containing the protein action is thought to move with respect to another set of larger filaments ($\sim$ 100–120 Å) containing another fibrous protein, myosin. The events at the molecular level which lead to this transposition of

material are not at present clear; these events may of course be
due to molecular folding at the micro level. It is at present not
clear how and where the driving forces are generated. Biochemical
asymmetry is needed within the system if the movement is to be
unidirectional, as has been recognized for some time (11).

The objective of this paper is not so much to discuss the nature
of the primary contractile event now envisioned for skeletal muscle
as it is to describe the structure and possible functions of other
fibrous protein systems of muscle which are thought to be coupled
to the contractile process. A brief discussion of the latter will be
included for background. For our purposes, muscle function will
be separated into two classes, (a) those functions associated with
the performance of mechanical work, and (b) those functions concerned more with the conservation of stored mechanical energy.
The latter class of functions must be clarified, since it is usually
not included in discussions of muscle function. Muscles can be
thought of as "tension generators" as well as work generators (12).
In isometric contractions, muscles develop tension with little change
in external dimensions; thus any work performed must be internal.
In this case, work is done against an elastic element, the series
elastic element, which is extended by the contractile elements as
contraction proceeds (13). At the peak of contraction, energy is
stored in the series elastic element, which is released in the form
of heat as the muscle relaxes. The unit contraction of skeletal
muscle is the twitch and represents the contractile response coupled
with a cycle of activation by way of the membrane. Tension is not
maintained in skeletal muscles for any appreciable time beyond
the decay of the active state. In many cases, however, tension can
be maintained in the absence of the active state for prolonged
periods of time; for example, in the tonic contractions of certain
molluscan muscles, it is maintained for periods of days or weeks
(16). It is in the latter cases that the conservative functions of
muscles are most clearly seen. It is entirely possible that a mechanism similar to that in molluscan muscles is present in other
muscles which have a tonic function.

It is of course possible to maintain tension by continually re-
cycling the contractile system. This is the way in which striated
muscles maintain tetanic contractions. Stated in other terms, the
active state of the muscle is maintained by continued reactivation
of the muscle at a level which will keep the series elastic component

stretched. This method of tension maintenance requires the continuous turnover of metabolic energy, and the cost of tension maintenance per unit time is related to, although it may not be as large as, the initial expenditure during tension development (14). An alternate possibility is the conversion of the contractile material itself into an inextensible body, or the substitution of a parallel inextensible element for the contractile system at the peak of contraction. Tension could be maintained at a level above resting tension as long as the parallel element is stiff. If the substituted element is much less extensible than the series elastic element, the tension maintained by this system will remain close to peak contractile tension. Furthermore, if no metabolic energy is required to maintain the elastic state of the parallel element, no metabolic energy would be expended during the prolonged contraction, resulting in a tremendous increase in the over-all economy of contraction.

A system of the latter type was proposed many years ago to account for the ability of molluscan adductor muscles to remain contracted for prolonged periods of time. Grutzner (15) and von Uexkull (16) proposed what was called a "catch mechanism" to explain such phenomenon. The earlier literature has been reviewed by Bayliss (17). Recent evidence mostly derived from studies on the anterior byssus retractor muscle (ABRM) of *Mytilus edulis,* a catch muscle, clearly rules out the active contraction of this muscle as the basis for prolonged contractions, thus necessitating the postulation of a conservative mechanism of the type described above (for evidence, see discussion below).

ORGANIZATION OF THE FIBROUS PROTEINS IN MUSCLES

The molecular weights and dimensions of muscle fibrous proteins are given in Table I. There is little doubt that the performance of mechanical work in all muscles so far examined is associated with the actomyosin system. Both actin and myosin are required for the contractile process (18) and metabolic energy is in all likelihood fed into the system by way of hydrolysis of adenosine triphosphate (ATP). The enzymatic sites located on the heavy meromyosin fraction of the myosin molecule may be the sites at which this occurs *in vivo*. This topic has been extensively reviewed during the past few years (19).

The location of actin and myosin within the myofilaments has been the object of a number of recent studies; the results on skeletal muscles of the vertebrates clearly indicate that myosin is located in the A, or anisotropic bands (20), although each of the subfractions of myosin, the heavy and light meromyosins, seem to be localized in distinctly different portions of this band (21). These studies, using antibodies against myosin and its subfractions,

TABLE I
DIMENSIONS OF FIBROUS PROTEINS IN MUSCLE
[Modified from Cohen and Szent-Györgyi (34)]

Major fibrous protein	Molecular weight	Estimated length	Estimated axial ratio
Actin	57,000[a]–74,000[b]	290[b]	12[b]
Myosin	450,000[c, d, e, f,]–620,000[g]	1600	50
Myosin fractions			
a. HMM	230,000[h]–330,000 (43)	400[h]	15–20[h]
b. LMM	96,000[h]–140,000 (43)	550[h]	30–40[h]
Tropomyosin	53,000[i]	385[i]	25[i]
Paramyosin	134,000 (38)–225,000[j]	1400 (38)	80 (38)

[a] Mommaerts, W. F. M. F., *J. Biol. Chem.* **198**, 445 (1952).
[b] Tsao, T. C., *Biochim. et Biophys. Acta* **11**, 227 (1953).
[c] Laki, K., and Caroll, W. R., *Nature* **175**, 389 (1955).
[d] Holtzer, H., and Lowey, S. *J. Am. Chem. Soc.* **78**, 5955 (1956).
[e] Mommaerts, W. F. M. F., and Aldrich, B. B., *Science* **126**, 1294 (1957).
[f] Gergely, J., and Kohler, H., "Conference on Chemistry of Muscular Contraction, Tokyo," p. 14. Igaku Shoin, Ltd., Tokyo, 1958.
[g] Keilley, W. W., and Harrington, W. F., *Biochim. et Biophys. Acta* **41**, 401 (1960).
[h] Szent-Györgyi, A. G., *Arch. Biochem. Biophys.* **42**, 35 (1953).
[i] Tsao, T. C., Bailey, K., and Adair, G. S., *Biochem. J.* **40**, 27 (1951).
[j] Lowey, S., Holtzer, H., and Kucera, C., in preparation. See also (42).

indicate that myosin migrates laterally during contraction. This finding suggests that the protein constituents of the large A filaments do not remain fixed, requiring a modification of the sliding filament hypothesis which is consistent with both the morphological and biochemical and in addition the recent immunological data. However, Szent-Györgyi has recently proposed that this migration of the myosin fractions within the A band might actually be the morphological basis for contraction; the folding of an extended myosin molecule within the A filament on one side of the

A band may draw in the small filament out of the I band on the other side, shortening the I band without necessarily changing the length of the A band (*22, 22a*). Movements in the position of the myosin fractions during the various stages of contraction have been found by Tunic and Holzer, using antibody techniques (*23*).

There is at present good morphological evidence to the effect that actin is located in the small 50-Å filaments which occupy the I bands and interdigitate with the large filaments in the A band. Recently, it has been shown by Hansen (*24*) that the F-actin filament (fibrous form of actin) is a double-stranded array of actin monomers. The small 50-Å filaments also have a beaded appearance in electron microscopic pictures of muscle and are quite similar to pictures of F-actin preparations. Oosowa (*25*) has, on the other hand, suggested two forms of polymerization in F-actin. One form is a three-stranded, helical array of monomers which this worker believes is identical to the long molecular chains found in F-actin solutions; the other form is a linear array of actin monomers. Oosawa presents an argument based on physical principles for the belief that the three-stranded form is the most stable form of the F-actin chain, i.e., has the lowest free energy and would thus be the preferred form.

It has been known for some time that F-actin contains bound nucleotide and that during the formation of F-actin from G-actin, ATP bound to the latter is dephosphorylated (*26, 26a*). The significance of this bound nucleotide is not clear, although it seems reasonable to suggest that it plays a role in the energetics of the contractile process [see the hypothesis recently proposed by Carlson and Siger (*26b*)]. Limitations to this suggestion have been recently pointed out by Hayashi and Rosenblueth (*26c*).

In muscles previously classified as smooth muscles, localization of the fibrous proteins has not been nearly as well worked out as in skeletal muscles. Many patterns of filamentous organization are found in these muscles and, as mentioned above, this category contains a vast collection of muscle types.

In the molluscan adductors and byssus retractors, filaments of two sizes have been described (*27, 28*). The small filaments are about the same size as those found in striated muscles, that is, ~ 50 Å. The large filaments are, however, much larger than those found in striated muscle. The diameter may approach 1000 Å. Since the patterns of organization of molluscan myofilaments are unfamiliar to most readers, Figs. 1 and 2 are included to illustrate the typical array of these filaments. Hanson and Lowry have found that in the transparent portion of the adductor of the oyster, the filaments are longitudinally organized in a pattern reminiscent of the organization in striated muscles (27). In this particular muscle, the large filaments are discontinuous, although they are not regularly aligned longitudinally in a striated pattern. The small filaments are regularly arranged around the large filaments, but not in a hexagonal array as is typical of vertebrate striated muscles. Structural patterns present in some of the other invertebrate muscles have been recently reviewed by Hanson and Lowy (29). Note that the small filaments in Figs. 1 and 2 are not independent of one another but seem to form a network around the large filaments.

In mammalian smooth muscles, the structure of the myofilaments has been only recently examined (30, 31). Small filaments of the order of 50–70 Å in diameter have been observed; no large filaments are seen. The small filaments are often interrupted at intervals by darkly staining regions, called dark bodies, which are thought to be homologous to the Z line of skeletal muscles. However, the possibility exists that they might be analogous to contraction bands in skeletal muscles.

The continuity of the filaments in many of the nonstriated muscles is still open to question. In striated muscles, both large and small filaments are discontinuous in presently available micrographs. This is also no doubt the case in the oyster transparent adductor. However, in mammalian smooth muscles, discontinuity has not been demonstrated. The filaments in such muscles may form a continuous network as is suggested in the picture of molluscan muscle shown in Fig. 2. Grimestone et al. (32) have found continuous networks in the retractor muscles of Metridium. The question of continuity of myofilaments in the molluscan muscles will be discussed later, since it is intimately tied in with the nature of the catch mechanism in these muscles.

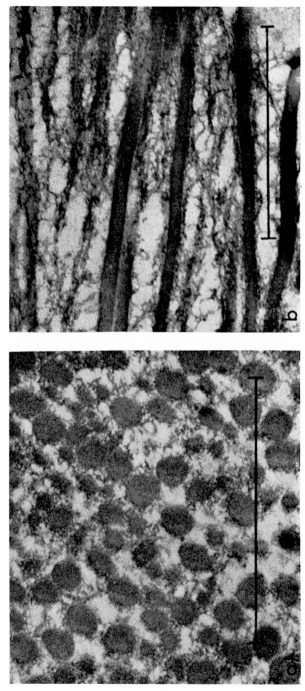

146

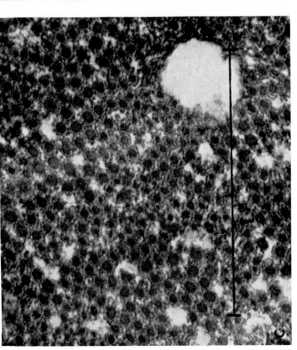

Fig. 1. Organization of myofilaments in two portions of the adductor muscle of *Mercenaria mercenaria*, the common quahog. (a) and (b) show cross sections and longitudinal sections of the white portion; (c) and (d) show the same for the tinted portion of the adductor. Note the increase in size of the large filaments in the white portion. This part of the muscle is relatively rich in the protein paramyosin and has a pronounced tonic function. Note also the network around the large filaments made up of small filaments. From micrographs published by Philpott *et al.* (28).

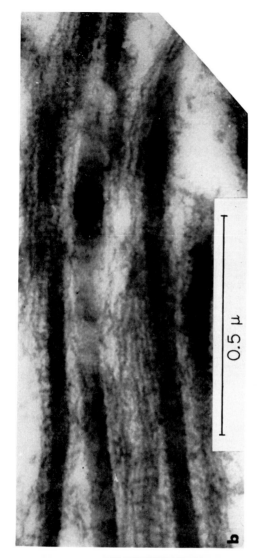

0.5 μ

FIG. 2. Three micrographs of longitudinal sections of myofilaments from the anterior byssus retractor muscle of *Mytilus edulis*, a catch muscle for which a great deal of physiological data are available. Note the apparent network formed by the small filaments along the surface of the large filaments. Details of large and small myofilaments are shown in (a) and (b). Living muscles were fixed in osmium tetroxide, stained in PTA and imbedded in 1:3 methyl:butyl methacrylate. (Unpublished photographs by W. H. Johnson.)

149

OTHER FUNCTIONS OF FIBROUS PROTEINS IN MUSCLE

Aside from collagen, which is present in most, if not all, muscles, there are two other fibrous proteins extracted from muscles in amounts of 10% or more of the extractable fibrous proteins which have been clearly identified and for which functions have at least been postulated. These are tropomyosin and paramyosin. A discussion of other components can be found in Perry's review (33). Tropomyosin is found in most muscles and usually makes up about 10–12% of the total protein (33). Paramyosin, on the other hand, has been found only in invertebrate muscles; it is present in large quantities in those muscles which have a pronounced catch function (35).

Both tropomyosin and paramyosin are resistant to denaturation by ethanol. As a matter of fact, this resistance is used in the isolation of the proteins. Tropomyosin is isolated by treating muscles previously dried in ethanol with solutions of high ionic strength. Paramyosin is isolated from extracts of molluscan muscles by treatment with 70% ethanol. Actomyosin, and no doubt many other components, are denatured by the ethanol, and paramyosin can be readily isolated from the precipitate thus formed. In this respect, one of the subfractions of myosin is similar to tropomyosin and paramyosin. Light meromyosin can be fractionated in ethanol to yield a component which has many properties similar to paramyosin and tropomyosin. These properties have been discussed in some detail by Szent-Györgyi and Cohen (34).

The molecular weights and sizes of these proteins are also listed in Table I. A comment must be made with respect to the nomenclature which is currently in use, since it might give rise to some confusion. Paramyosin has been classed by some workers as a tropomyosin; more specifically, it has been called tropomyosin A (35, 49). The water-soluble tropomyosin obtained from most muscles has been designated as tropomyosin B. This usage is based largely on the similarities which exist between the amino acid composition of the two proteins. However, as Hodge (36) has pointed out, other differences, such as those appearing in crystalline patterns exhibited by the precipitated proteins, suggest that one should be cautious in classing these proteins together. The gross amino acid composition may be similar, but, as is obvious from most biochemical studies on proteins, the sequence and tertiary structure of the protein may be of much greater importance in determining functional properties than the relative amounts of the various amino acids. A recent report has appeared in which it is proposed that the crystalline fraction of myosin, light meromyosin fraction I, is the analog in striated muscles of paramyosin (37); this conclusion was also based on a similarity in the amino acid composition of these proteins. But more complete identity of the properties of molecules must be demonstrated before one can conclude that there are fundamental similarities between the fibrous proteins of various muscles.

It is premature to speculate extensively on whether or not the many similarities in these proteins or protein fractions have functional significance. Tropomyosin may play a role similar to that of paramyosin, which has now been implicated in the catch mechanism. This has been suggested by several workers (see Perry's review, 33). Since paramyosin has clearly been associated with this important aspect of muscle function, the evidence for this association and some thoughts regarding the way in which paramyosin performs this function will serve as the focus of attention in the remainder of this paper.

Early measurements of the molecular weight of paramyosin gave the figure of 140,000 (38). On using 1400 Å as the molecular length, a value that seems to be well substantiated, it can be easily shown that portions of the molecule would have to be in the form of single helices if the molecular weight were this low (38). This would mean that the stability of the molecule in these regions would not be great; charge interactions, for instance, tend to disrupt the helical structure in regions where a single-stranded helix is present, as is the case in polyglutamic acid (39). There is little doubt that paramyosin, in solution, has the shape of a rod; the axial ratio of the molecule is high, around 80, and the intrinsic viscosity is that which would be expected of a solution of rigid rods (38). Yet, in studies reported thus far, there is no evidence that the molecular shape changes as the pH is varied; in fact, it would appear that there is little if any change in the length of the paramyosin molecule in going from neutral pH to values below 5.0 (paramyosin is insoluble in the range between 5.0 and approximately 6.5–7.0; see below). Although his measurements did not permit specification of length with great precision, Hodge (40) found a molecular length of approximately 1400 Å at the lower pH.

Kay found the same length at neutral pH (38). This evidence would thus favor the view that the paramyosin rod is stable over this pH range. Measurements of the optical rotation and the anomalous rotatory dispersion (Cotton effect) of paramyosin in the native form and in the presence of 8 M urea indicate that some regions of the helix are relatively stable (34, 41). In myosin and tropomyosin, for instance, the helix content is reduced to zero in the presence of 8 M urea, whereas the helix content of paramyosin is reduced from 90% to 28% (41). Compare data on paramyosin and poly-L-glutamic acid in the last reference.

Recent measurements of the molecular weight of paramyosin have indicated that it is closer to 220,000, and x-ray studies have suggested the presence of a coiled coil, which would be consistent with the idea that paramyosin is a two-stranded helix (42, and Lowey, Holtzer, and Kucera, personal communication, June 1962). The revised molecular weight figure is large enough to avoid the difficulties mentioned above. On using an average amino acid residue weight of 114 (38), approximately 2000 amino acid residues would be required to give a molecular weight of 220,000. The length of an α-helix containing 1000 residues would be ∼ 1400 Å. Thus two coiled together, or packed side by side, would give the molecular dimensions of paramyosin. There is ample reason to assume as a model, in consideration of intermolecular interactions between paramyosin molecules, a rigid cylindrical rod which does not change shape as the pH or the ionic strength of the solution is changed, at least within the limits referred to below in the discussion of the functional role of paramyosin, i.e., pH 5.0–8.0 and ionic strength 0.05–0.6. The rod may be stabilized by nonpolar residue interactions between the two helices, similar to Crick's "knob in hole" packing in α-proteins (see 43).

Tropomyosin and paramyosin are unique among the fibrous proteins of muscle in that they form very regular crystallites when precipitated under certain conditions (see 36 for review of these types). Myosin does not form such crystallites; however, one of the subfractions of myosin, light meromyosin fraction I, does form regular crystalline precipitates (44). The crystallites formed by paramyosin are needle-shaped, whereas those formed by tropomyosin have regular edges and faces and are in the form of plates. In the electron microscope, tropomyosin exhibits a regular periodic pattern consisting of an open net. The main periodicity is about 400 Å. In Fig. 3 are shown some of the patterns exhibited by paramyosin and tropomyosin crystals.

Paramyosin also exhibits regular patterns in the electron microscope, the precise character of which depends on the conditions under which the crystallite was formed. Hodge has reviewed these patterns in a recent publication (36; see Fig. 3 of this paper). At low pH (~ 4.5), a major period of 1400 Å with several subperiods was obtained. Hodge has suggested that this particular pattern arises from an antiparallel alignment of the molecules similar to the fibrous long spacing (FLS) pattern of collagen. At neutral pH several patterns have been obtained, showing periods of 70, 140, and 720 Å. Locker and Schmitt (45) have observed periods of 360 and 1800 Å in some preparations. These findings suggest that, under many different conditions, the individual molecules interact in such a way that their ends are shifted with respect to one another by some integral fraction of the molecular length.

The most common repeat is the 140-Å repeat, which may be due to the presence of interacting sites, or at least of sites which take up heavy metal stains, at intervals of $1/10$ of the molecular length. These sites, of course, may be more sparsely distributed, say at intersite distances of $1/5$ of the molecular length, but they would have to be distributed at regular intervals in any case in order to give this regular spacing.

It has been suggested that, in collagen, the band pattern is due to the presence of small segments of the molecule in which certain amino acids are concentrated. Kuhn (46) has presented evidence that arginine is the amino acid which interacts with phosphotungstic acid; thus a regular band pattern in preparations stained with this reagent would indicate that the guanidino groups of arginine are concentrated in certain well-defined regions of the molecule. Uranyl acetate is apparently taken up by anionic groups, such as the α-carboxyl group on glutamic acid. Regular band patterns are also obtained in collagen with the latter reagent. Thus the possibility exists that regular sequences of a specific amino acid occur along the length of those fibrous proteins which exhibit regular periodic patterns; certain groups, such as arginine, may be concentrated in certain regions. In coiled-coil proteins, these groups would have to appear in a regular primary structural sequence

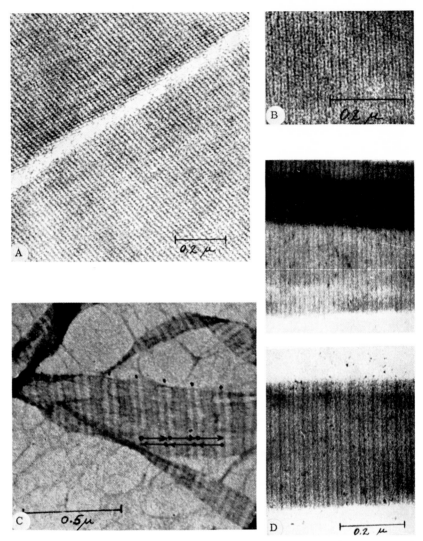

FIG. 3. Patterns shown by tropomyosin and paramyosin crystals when stained with PTA. (A) Rabbit tropomyosin crystal fixed in osmium tetroxide, stained with PTA and imbedded in n-butyl methacrylate. Main spacing is 200 Å. (B) Rabbit tropomyosin crystal deposited on a supporting film and stained with PTA. The main spacing is 200 Å. (C) Fibrils reconstituted from a paramyosin solution under acid conditions. Hodge has interpreted the main spacing as due to antiparallel packing of rodlike molecules 1400 Å long. (D) Two fibrils from a paramyosin "crystal" formed by reducing the ionic strength of an approximately neutral paramyosin solution. The main spacing in the upper picture is 145 Å, while in the lower picture the pattern is complex with a fundamental repeat of $5 \times 145 = 725$ Å. From Hodge (36) with permission of the author.

with other smaller groups so that the former would protrude from the surface of the molecular cylinder, while the latter occupy the internal space of the molecule (see Waugh, *46a*).

Hodge (*47*) has pointed out that paramyosin does not form patterns analogous of the segment long spacing in collagen which, in the latter case, has served as a sort of molecular fingerprint.

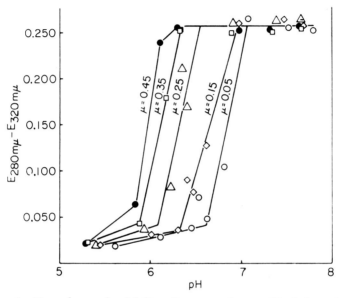

FIG. 4. Dependence of solubility of paramyosin on pH of the solution. The difference in absorption (E) at 280 mμ and 320 mμ is a measure of the protein content of the supernatant following centrifugation of the solution (initial protein concentration the same in all cases); pH is given on the abscissa. Note sharp zone of precipitation and its dependence on ionic strength (μ). From W. H. Johnson *et al.* (*53*) with permission of *Science.*

The reason for this may lie in the pattern of charge interactions in paramyosin during crystallization. The solubility of paramyosin is very sensitive to pH and ionic strength, an effect which is strikingly abrupt on the pH scale (see Fig. 4), suggesting that charge interactions are very important in the formation of aggregates of this molecule. If the molecules are held apart in solution by repulsive electrostatic forces, due to the presence of aggregates of glutamic or aspartic acid, then, as the pH is lowered through the range in which such groups associate with protons, the surface charge will drop and the net repulsive force would decrease. Since rod-shaped molecules tend to become aligned in solutions at moderate to high concentration even in the absence of strong intermolecular forces (48), the individual molecules, already aligned, would tend to aggregate as the net charge decreases. Since there are a number of arginine and lysine groups also present on paramyosine (49), as the negative charge density decreases, the net repulsive force may be converted into a net attractive force and molecular aggregation will be enhanced. Periodic fields along rods can give rise to attraction and repulsion depending on the magnitude of positive and negative contributions to the field (Oosawa, personal communication, 1962). If these charges are concentrated in regions which are evenly distributed along the molecule, positive groups would come to lie next to negatively charged groups during aggregation, and adjacent molecules would take up only a limited number of very specific positions with respect to one another. If, furthermore, the charged sites were spaced at equal distances along the molecule, and assuming of course that the same amino acid sequence is present in each molecule, the ends would never appear in register, but would be shifted with respect to each other, except perhaps when the molecules become lined up antiparallel to one another. The above discussion may seem to imply that electrostatic interactions alone are responsible for aggregation. Actually, little is known about the forces which stabilize the paramyosin crystal lattice, once it has formed. There is little doubt that if the molecules can pack closely together, van der Waal interactions and hydrogen bonding will play a role in stabilizing the lattice.

It appears that in many respects paramyosin is similar to tropocollagen, and the aggregation of paramyosin molecules may be due to a comparable site-specific interaction, that is, specific groups coming to lie next to other groups, giving rise to well-defined, long-range patterns. The striking difference between the two is the ease of reversibility of the effect in paramyosin; alteration of the pH breaks up the lattice pattern but it can be obtained again by returning the pH to the original value. This reversibility may have a functional significance, as will be shown below. The functional role of collagen requires that the interactions holding the tropocollagen molecules together be rather stable, since to function properly in their environment, collagen fibrils must be relatively inert to changes in the extracellular environment.

PHYSIOLOGICAL FUNCTIONS OF THE FIBROUS PROTEINS OF MUSCLE

The functions of actin and myosin have been referred to above. There is little doubt that they are responsible for the performance of mechanical work by the muscle cell.

Tropomyosin is extracted in rather small but significant quantities from the muscle cell (approximately 10%). This, however, varies with the type of muscle. At one time it was suggested that the tropomyosin was a fragment of the myosin molecule (50). Lowey and Cohen (43) have suggested that it is a component of the large myofilaments of skeletal muscle, serving as a backbone upon which the myosin is deposited. There is as yet little direct evidence for these suggestions.

A functional role for paramyosin has been recently proposed by several workers (51, 52, 53). This protein is found in large quantities in the molluscan muscles which possess the capacity to maintain contractile tension for prolonged periods of time with little fatigue or utilization of metabolic energy stores. As an example of the magnitude of these effects, Parnas found in work done on the common clam, Venus, that the adductor muscles were able to keep the shells closed against a counterforce of 3–4 kg/cm^2 without a detectable increase in the oxygen utilization (54). Ritchie (55) has claimed that these effects can be explained on the basis of an increase in the economy of the muscle; that is, if each contraction were prolonged, fewer contractions would have to be summed to maintain contraction. But molluscan muscles are also capable of relatively fast relaxation; thus the central question has to do with the molecular basis for a specific increase in economy of these muscles during tonic contractions. Is it associated with a shift in the functional properties of the actomyosin which results in increased economy, or is a second protein system involved?

The question of the true economy of these muscles has not as yet been settled. Attempts have been made recently to measure the heat production of the catch muscles, as the molluscan muscles described above are called. The results have been limited by technical difficulties (as quoted in 56). Such results have indicated that the increase in heat output during prolonged contractions is much smaller than that occurring during initial phases of contraction when mechanical work is done. Other experiments, in which the anterior byssus retractor muscle (ABRM) of *Mytilus edulis*, a catch muscle, was exposed to solutions containing iodoacetic acid and an atmosphere containing nitrogen, indicate that the prolonged phase of contraction drew very little on the energy stores within the muscle cell (57). Such contractions did not exhaust the phosphogen stores of the muscle, which are the only reserves left after iodoacetate poisoning (assuming that the metabolic pathways in the ABRM are similar to those in skeletal muscles—a reasonable assumption). It has been clearly shown that the active state is not present during prolonged contractions (56, 58). The active state disappears very soon after the cessation of the stimulus, but the tension developed by the muscle remains high for a considerable period. In addition, a large increase in the elastic modulus accompanies the catch state (56, 58, 59); the latter term has been applied to the stage of tension maintenance during which the active state is absent. The muscle also shows less plastic flow under load than it does at rest. Jewell (56) has designated this state as the fused state since, in his experiments, the muscle appeared to have become vulcanized as the result of tonic stimulation. These changes in mechanical properties are in fact diagnostic of the catch state.

All of these findings clearly rule out active contraction during the catch state, and apparently the actomyosin system, or at least those phases of its function which are associated with the performance of mechanical work, cannot be involved in this state. Alternative explanations have appeared which invoke a change in time constant of decay of tension within the actomyosin system itself (60), or, on the other hand, the similarity of the catch state to rigor mortis in some of its aspects has led to the proposal that the catch state might be a sort of reversible rigor (77). In our laboratory we have obtained evidence which has led us to the proposal that paramyosin is involved in the maintenance of tension in the catch state. Ruegg has independently arrived at a similar conclusion (52).

As mentioned above, the diagnostic feature of the catch state is the large increase in elastic modulus of the muscle which accompanies it. This can be seen in Fig. 5. Good estimates of this increase are difficult to obtain but it can be of the order of 10 or more times. There is no question that this effect, which was implicit in the results reported by Winton (61) some 30 years ago, is well established, and that the system which forms the molecular basis for this fact must be capable of undergoing a considerable change in elastic modulus which, furthermore, must be readily reversible. When the catch state is present the elastic modulus of the tension-bearing systems must increase, while during phasic contractions of the catch muscle (contractions in which the relaxation may be orders of magnitude faster than relaxation in the presence of the catch state—see Fig. 5 for characteristics of tonic and phasic contractions) the system must remain plastic and exten-

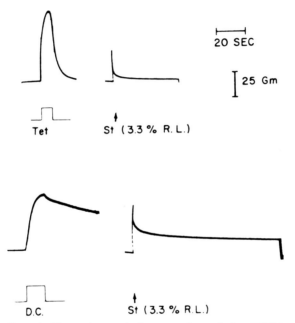

20 SEC

25 Gm

Tet   St (3.3 % R. L.)

D.C.   St (3.3 % R.L.)

FIG. 5. Records illustrating typical contractions of the ABRM are shown at the left. In the top record, a pulsed current (Tet) stimulus is used to elicit a phasic response. Note the duration of the relaxation phase. In the record below, the response to a depolarizing direct current (D.C.) stimulus is seen. Note prolonged relaxation. At the right are shown records of the time course of tension following quick stretch (St) [3.3% of the rest length (R.L.) of the muscle] during the period immediately following the two types of contractile responses. In the bottom record, the muscle was shortened approximately 5% before stretching to reduce the tension remainder to zero, thus both stretches start from essentially a zero base line. Note greater inextensibility (elastic modulus) of muscle following the DC stimulus. This record illustrates an effect on the mechanical properties which was first observed by Winton (61). W. H. Johnson in "Comparative Animal Physiology" (Prosser and Brown, eds.), p. 452. Saunders, Philadelphia, Pennsylvania, 1962, with permission.

sible, since during and following the relaxation phase of phasic responses, the muscle is very extensible.

One can prepare glycerinated fibers from catch muscles such as the ABRM in the manner originally worked out by Szent-Györgyi (62) for the psoas muscle. Such fibers will exhibit sizable contractions when ATP is added to the medium in the presence of magnesium (53), although the tensions developed during such contractions do not approach the tensions possible in the living muscle. Ruegg (52) has found that such fibers, allowed to shorten in ATP and magnesium, will develop much more tension than they did during contraction when they stretched back to their initial length. This extra tension remains in the presence of Salyrgan. This is taken to mean that the contractile system (actomyosin), active in ATP–Mg but poisoned by Salyrgan, is not involved in the development and maintenance of this extra tension. On the other hand, the system responsible for this extra tension has properties very similar to those of paramyosin. In fact artificial paramyosin threads will mimic many of these properties (Ruegg, 52).

In work which has been briefly reported (63) and which will be published in full shortly, we have examined the stress-strain curves of glycerinated fibers from the ABRM as a function of pH of the medium. We reported earlier (53) that the solubility of paramyosin is a function of the pH of the medium (Fig. 4). When the pH of a solution of paramyosin is lowered through the range 7–6.0, the protein precipitates out of solution and, if the change has been made slowly, needle-shaped crystals are formed. The contraction of glycerinated fibers in ATP is reduced sharply by lowering the pH of the medium to about 6.0 (53). This has been interpreted as being due to a retardation of contraction due to the presence in the contractile machinery of stiff paramyosin-containing rods at pH 6.0.

The stress-strain curve for a glycerinated fiber equilibrated at low pH (pH near 6.0) is relatively steep compared to the curve obtained when the pH is raised above the point where paramyosin, isolated as a purified protein, would pass into solution. The stress-strain curves follow the pH solubility dependence of paramyosin very nicely, the elastic modulus changing rather abruptly over a narrow range of pH in the region around pH 6.7. To obtain the full effect of lowered pH on the elastic modulus, the fiber often must be oriented mechanically by passing it through several cycles of stretch or by equilibrating in the low pH solution at a stretched length for 15 minutes or longer. Mechanical orientation of organic polymers is often necessary to produce crystallization, and with it, a higher elastic modulus. From this work there is little question that, in the glycerinated fiber, precipitation (or crystallization) of paramyosin by treating the fiber at low pH results in an increase in the elastic modulus and a decrease in the plastic flow of the loaded fiber. This change in properties is no doubt similar to the effects observed by Ruegg.

Ionic strength and temperature have effects on the elastic modulus as well (W. H. Johnson, unpublished results, 1961). These are similar to those which would be expected if paramyosin were the main component of the system underlying the above mentioned stress-strain behavior. An increase in ionic strength leads to a decrease in the elastic modulus, as does an increase in temperature. ATP and pyrophosphate have the effect of reducing the elastic modulus in the absence of magnesium (52), and when the pH of the medium is altered in the presence of pyrophosphate and magnesium, the drop in elastic modulus is larger than it is when the fiber is equilibrated in buffer only (63). There is little doubt that ATP and pyrophosphate, which are highly charged molecules, have an effect on the elastic modulus of the paramyosin component of the fiber, but there is evidence that part of the effect may be due to the plasticizing effect of these agents on the actomyosin component of the system. In our work, some of the effects obtained could be explained on this basis. This is especially true of fibers which were preshortened in ATP–Mg prior to the stress-strain tests.

These results lead not only to the conclusion that the paramyosin system is involved in the viscoelastic behavior of catch muscles but also that it is mechanically continuous. In order to obtain the pH-dependent stress-strain behavior described above in the presence of agents which plasticize the actomyosin system, the system responsible must be mechanically continuous and must operate in parallel with the actomyosin system. We have developed a model shown in Fig. 6 consisting of three mechanical elements, one containing paramyosin, another actomyosin, and the third consisting of the series elastic components of the muscle. In this model, the first two elements are in parallel with each other but coupled to a series elastic element which is common to both (both are attached at one end to this element). Passive maintenance of tension beyond the decay of the active state in isometric contractions of the living muscle can be explained by this model if it is assumed that the paramyosin system undergoes a phase change (perhaps crystallization) at the peak of the contraction, resulting in the formation

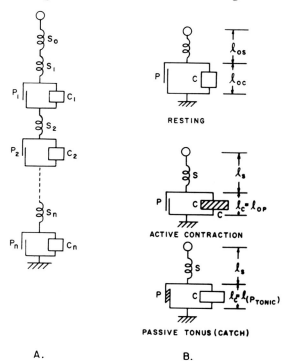

A.   B.

Fig. 6. A model of how the paramyosin system might act to maintain tension during an isometric tonic contraction. At the left is shown a series array of series elastic elements (S_1), contractile elements (C_1), and paramyosin elements (P_1) as they might be arranged in the muscle cell. At the right, these elements are shown in a lumped model. During active contraction, the contractile element shortens, lengthening the series elastic element, thus giving rise to isometric tension. As the muscle passes into the catch state, the paramyosin crystallizes, thus keeping the series elastic element elongated and the tension near peak contractile tension. From W. H. Johnson (64), with permission of Physiological Reviews.

of inextensible rods within the muscle. Stresses developed in the series elastic element by the contracting actomyosin system are transferred to the paramyosin system as the active state decays. These stresses can be maintained (essentially the series elastic element can be kept almost fully stretched) if following the phase change the elastic modulus of the paramyosin system is much larger than that of the series elastic element. The model explains how tension can be maintained for long periods of time without the necessity of continual energy input. Aside from the energy which may be needed to produce the phase change, which may be comparable to crystallization of paramyosin from solution and would thus require energy equivalent to a latent heat of crystallization, little energy would be needed to maintain the resulting state of the paramyosin. A full description of this model will appear shortly (64).

A POSSIBLE CHANGE IN MYOFILAMENT STRUCTURE UNDERLYING THE CATCH FUNCTION

The above alteration in elastic modulus with parameters such as pH may be analogous to, or may actually have a basis identical to, the change in the elastic modulus observed as the living molluscan muscle passes into the catch state. The parameters responsible for the change may differ in the glycerinated fiber and in the living muscle. Relaxation following tonic stimulation in the living muscle is usually faster than tension decay following stretch of a glycerinated fiber at low pH (W. H. Johnson, unpublished observations, 1961). The former is also quite variable and probably depends on the functional characteristics of the system which controls the catch system. The controlling system probably hastens relaxation when activated. Takahashi has obtained evidence for a second neuromuscular system which controls the rate of relaxation in these muscles (65, 66). The rate of relaxation can be altered from that characteristic of the catch state to that characteristic of a phasic contraction by adding small concentrations of 5-hydroxytryptamine (67). The controlling parameter in the living muscle may not be pH or ionic strength, but it is certainly a strong possibility that the changes in viscoelastic properties in living and glycerinated fibers may have a common origin in the paramyosin system. Ruegg has recently been able to demonstrate the catch state in the presence of reagents which functionally remove the actomyosin system (68).

One can but speculate on the nature of the phase change which may occur in the living muscle and which no doubt occurs in the glycerinated fiber as the pH of the medium is changed. The crystallization of paramyosin from solution in the same pH range can

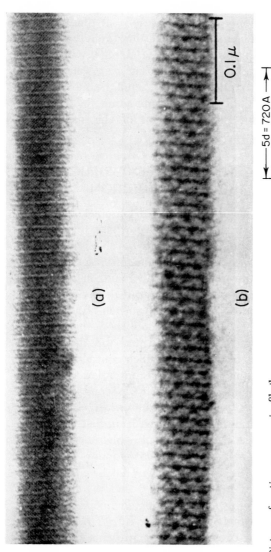

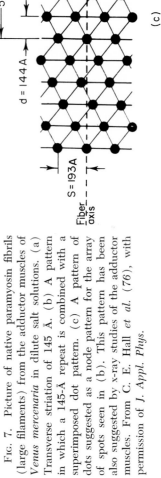

Fig. 7. Picture of native paramyosin fibrils (large filaments) from the adductor muscles of *Venus mercenaria* in dilute salt solutions. (a) Transverse striation of 145 Å. (b) A pattern in which a 145-Å repeat is combined with a superimposed dot pattern. (c) A pattern of dots suggested as a node pattern for the array of spots seen in (b). This pattern has been also suggested by x-ray studies of the adductor muscles. From C. E. Hall *et al.* (76), with permission of *J. Appl. Phys.*

164

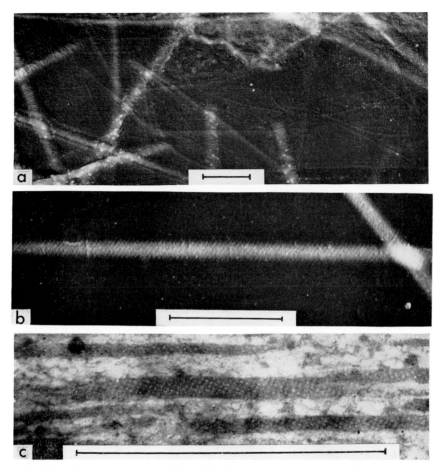

FIG. 8. Micrographs (a and b) of shadowed specimens prepared from suspensions of myofilaments from *Mercenaria mercenaria*. In a, the suspension was obtained by blendoring the muscle in solutions of low ionic strength. In b, the suspension was extracted at higher salt concentrations (0.5 M KCl) with the pH being kept near 6.0. Note that only a few of the small filaments seen in a are present in b. Under the conditions used in the latter, actomyosin is no doubt extracted, but paramyosin extraction is suppressed. Note the clear paramyosin periodicity in b. In c is shown a micrograph of a myofilament from a glycerinated anterior byssus retractor muscle of the blue mussel *Mytilus edulis*. This preparation was fixed and stained in osmic acid–PTA and embedded in methyl-butyl methacrylate. The open net structure seen here, which is apparently one of the modifications of paramyosin packing, has also been reported by Elliott; see Hansen and Lowy (29) (a and b, courtesy of D. Philpott and A. G. Szent-Györgyi; c, unpublished micrograph of W. H. Johnson).

certainly be thought of as a phase change, and the increase in intermolecular bonding which accompanies crystallization would in turn result in an increase of elastic modulus of the crystal. However, there are certain differences between paramyosin in solution and paramyosin in the large myofilaments which deserve attention. Paramyosin in the myofilament does not pass into solution as the pH is raised at low ionic strength (69), whereas, in solution, crystallites of paramyosin readily dissolve under comparable conditions (53). There are thus constraints within the myofilament which hold the paramyosin in place. Either these constraints are due to the presence of actomyosin, which must be located on the outside of the large filament (69), or the constraints may be internal. Paramyosin may be held on a framework of inert protein or, on the other hand, there may be a certain amount of cross-linking among the paramyosin molecules themselves which is not pH-sensitive. There is no evidence from work on isolated paramyosin for formation of this kind of stable cross linkages in crystallites. Thus the protein in the filaments must be held in place by other means.

See Figs. 7 and 8 for similarities in structure between crystallites and the large myofilaments. Figure 7 shows the netlike structure which Hall, Jakus, and Schmitt observed as a pattern of dots. Subsequent x-ray evidence also suggested that the large filaments were organized in this fashion. Recently we have been able to show that the stress-strain behavior of glycerinated fibers extracted with modified Hasselbach-Schneider solutions at pH 6.2 is virtually identical to that of unextracted fibers (70). Hasselbach-Schneider solutions are known to extract the myosin from glycerinated preparations of striated muscles (20) and will, at pH 6.2, extract the ATPase-containing protein from glycerinated preparations of the ABRM, leaving behind most of the paramyosin (69). The pH effects on the stress-strain curves of such extracted fibers are reversible, indicating that paramyosin does not pass into solution under conditions where the fiber has a low elastic modulus (at pH above 7.0). Paramyosin must be held in place in the myofilament by something other than the actomyosin and thus presumably by the framework of the myofilament.

Additional evidence for some sort of cross-linked framework is seen in the finding that glycerinated fibers of the ABRM exhibit small changes in baseline tension with changes in pH of the medium (W. H. Johnson, unpublished observations, 1962). These changes are reversible and are not related in any way to contraction in the presence of ATP; rather, they are similar to those that accompany latent volume changes in polymer systems (71). As an oriented polymer system swells laterally, tension is exerted along the axis of orientation, but this tension is not observed if the system is not sufficiently cross-linked to bear the stresses. In the absence of cross linkage, the system will undergo plastic flow and cannot sustain the tension developed as the system swells. That such tension changes in glycerinated ABRM fibers are reversible with pH and since the tension is maintained at a given pH indicates the presence of some degree of cross linkage within the myofilament; this cross linkage need not be between paramyosin molecules themselves, but may instead be present in the framework of the myofilament.

Evidence for the framework comes from two sources. Low angle x-ray patterns from molluscan catch muscles indicate that paramyosin may be organized in the form of ribbons or rodlets of approximately 100–120 Å in thickness or diameter (72). Bear and Selby (73) found evidence for rodlets in the large myofilaments of molluscan muscles, which, according to the x-ray evidence, were aligned either along the axis of the myofilament or at an angle of approximately 15 degrees with respect to this axis. The data favored the latter arrangement. Kahn and Johnson (69) found that when the paramyosin is extracted from the myofilaments of the ABRM, a residue is left behind which has the appearance of a string of beads. The interbead distance is ~ 720 Å, which is the unit cell length found in x-ray studies (73). These effects of extraction are seen in Fig. 9. The beadlike structures may thus form the basis of the unit cell structure of the filament, although it must be borne in mind that paramyosin precipitated from neutral solutions may also give this periodicity when examined in the electron microscope. However, the periodicity in the latter case has a different appearance than it does in extracted fibers. (Compare Fig. 9 with Fig. 3.)

If the paramyosin is held in place by a framework which is apparently inert and does not itself undergo changes with pH, then any repulsive forces operating between the paramyosin molecules must actually push these molecules apart against the constraints imposed by the framework. Certainly the paramyosin molecules must be held firmly enough so that the forces tending to disperse

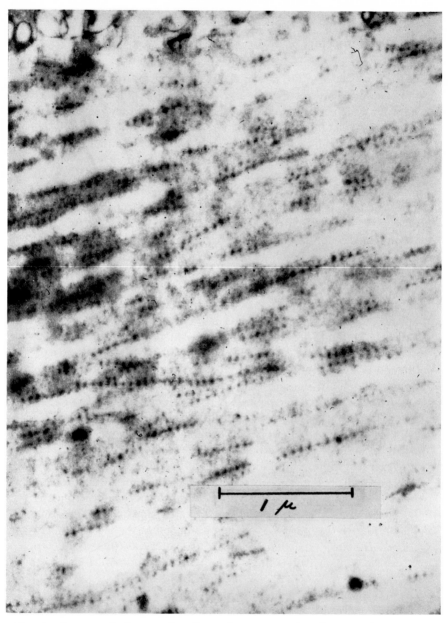

Fig. 9. Micrograph showing the effects of extraction of a glycerinated ABRM with alkaline pH (7.8). Hasselbach-Schneider solutions. Note the appearance of beaded structures which presumably represent the backbone structure of the large myofilaments in these muscles. From J. S. Kahn and W. H. Johnson (69).

168

them do not drive them out of the framework, otherwise the system would disperse with each phase change. In our experience, the elastic modulus of the glycerinated fiber quickly increases as the pH is lowered, even though full recovery of the high elastic modulus does not usually occur until the system has been reoriented by stretch. The latter findings suggest further that the molecules must be held in close juxtaposition to one another by the framework, so that crystallization can proceed at once after the dispersing forces have been reduced. This is somewhat comparable to seeding of supersaturated solutions. Full extent of crystallization will not be accomplished until the system is fully oriented, but the initial phases are enhanced by the constraints imposed on the paramyosin molecules by the framework of the myofilament.

Recent experiments of Hansen and Lowy (27) have indicated that the large filaments of molluscan muscles may not, in fact, be continuous. Examination of the cross-sectional area of large filaments in relaxed and tonically contracted muscles has indicated that the area does not change much, at least within the size categories selected by these workers. Also, large filaments isolated from homogenates of muscles such as the ABRM and examined in the electron microscope appear to be of a length far smaller than the length of the cells and, in some cases, appear to be tapered at the ends, suggesting that these filaments are discontinuous in the living muscle. One must assume, however, that isolation procedures have not produced alterations in the length of these filaments. Neither tapering nor discontinuities of the filaments have been observed in electron micrographs taken of muscles fixed in the living state. Paramyosin is located in the center of the large filaments, thus the morphological evidence of these workers would suggest discontinuity of the paramyosin system. However, the glycerinated-fiber work cited above cannot be reconciled with this view; the system is mechanically continuous and is capable of supporting tension in the absence of the actomyosin system. It can be readily seen that if the large filaments are indeed discontinuous in the living muscle, or have no mechanism by which they are linked together, mechanical continuity would necessarily involve the actomyosin system, since the only other filaments seen in micrographs are the small filaments. These are presumably composed of actin. Yet the bulk of evidence on the glycerinated fibers indicates that the actomyosin system seems not to be involved. Thus it is clear that, as in the case of skeletal muscles, morphological data have raised fundamental questions regarding the function of this system, questions which can only be resolved by a much closer look at the system.

It is doubtful that the high elastic moduli exhibited by glycerinated fibers of the ABRM at low pH could be due to fortuitous aggregation of the paramyosin filaments. These moduli are comparable to those observed in the living muscle in the tonic state. From data published by Jewell (56) for the tonic state of the muscle, the elastic modulus is of the order of 2×10^8 dynes/cm^2; that of a glycerinated fiber at low pH is in many cases near this value (W. H. Johnson, unpublished data, 1961). It is unlikely that spurious coalescence of filaments would lead to such high values of the elastic modulus.

To summarize, there is a distinct possibility that the paramyosin located in the large filaments of molluscan muscles is involved in tonic functions, and thus that the increase in elastic modulus observed when a living muscle passes into the catch state (or prolonged, tonic contraction) may have as a basis a change in the state of paramyosin.

Putting the known behavior of paramyosin together with its apparent organization within the large filament, one emerges with the following picture. In solution, paramyosin is a rather rigid molecule having the form of a cynder from which charged groups protrude. From the patterns found in paramyosin crystals, these groups are located in well-defined spots along the surface of the cylinder and are arranged so that molecules can pack closely together. At pH values below the precipitation point of paramyosin (mentioned above), repulsive electrostatic forces due to carboxy amino acid residues may be small enough to allow close approach of the molecules, already oriented by the tendency of long asymmetric molecules to orient in tactoidal arrangements (71). In fact, as the pH is lowered, association of protons with the acidic groups may change the pattern of charge interaction from a net repulsive force to a net attractive force, and the coalescence of the molecules may be enhanced by long-range electrostatic forces. If the double layer due to small ion countercharges is changed by changing the ionic strength, the molecules would tend to aggregate at different pH values; this is the case in paramyosin solutions. The entire interaction may be electrostatic, although there is no reason to believe that these forces are the only ones stabilizing the paramyosin filament system.

Turning to the structure of the large filament, paramyosin is no doubt located in the center of the filament, perhaps packed into subfilaments or ribbons. The paramyosin molecules may be constrained to remain in this matrix by another non-paramyosin component which appears when paramyosin is removed [the beadlike structure observed by Kahn and Johnson (69)]. Myosin is probably located on the surface of the large myofilament, since a core of paramyosin remains after removal of the myosin. The small 50-Å filaments observed in molluscan muscles as well as striated muscles probably consist of actin.

The actin-myosin reaction itself in all probability operates in the same way as it does in striated muscles, that is, the basic contractile response is an actin-myosin interaction; however, the relative movement of the myosin partner may cause a shift in the paramyosin matrix, especially if the conditions are such that the molecules in the latter have moved apart due to dissociative forces, i.e., where the net force between them is repulsive. This shift in the paramyosin matrix, which could be either a shift in the molecular lattice or a shift along "slip planes" or dislocations in the lattice, could then be "frozen" in place by altering conditions to those in which paramyosin crystallizes. This "freezing in" of the lattice could maintain the muscle at the length to which the myosin-actin contraction had brought it, thus maintaining tension under isometric conditions where the length change was internal and the series elastic element was stretched, or, in isotonic conditions, resisting the return under load to rest length. The change in mechanical properties associated with the "freezing in" of the paramyosin lattice would be that which is observed during tonic contractions, i.e., an increase of elastic modulus and a decrease in irreversible plastic flow under load.

The extent to which the change in the paramyosin lattice represents a true phase change must be decided by doing further thermodynamic studies on the system. In many respects, this system behaves like Kuhn's polyelectrolyte systems (6). The small tension changes with pH mentioned above suggest a similarity between these systems. However, the main function of the paramyosin system seems to be the conservation of mechanical energy rather than the performance of mechanical work. It is rather the change in viscoelastic properties associated with the phase change which is central in its function.

A complete change in phase of the entire system may not be necessary to achieve this. It may only be necessary to open up a small portion of the spaces between molecules to provide for the necessary change in mechanical properties; this may be more like the appearance of dislocation planes in a metallic crystal than the total melting of a polymer crystal. One might indeed observe a great deal of local or perhaps even long-range order in x-ray pictures of myofilaments in muscles which are not in the catch state, simply because in such circumstances the entire structure of the myofilament does not melt out. Only a small fraction of the total melts out to provide the necessary mechanical plasticity for the resting state.

It would be of interest to compare the above picture of the molluscan myofilament with that currently proposed for the large A filament of skeletal muscle. In the latter, myosin is also thought to occupy surface positions. Tropomyosin has been proposed as the core material. Recently Lowy and Cohen (43) have suggested that the fundamental myosin unit is a tactoid consisting of four myosin molecules. The light meromyosin (LMM) components of the four myosins interact to form a rodlike structure with the heavy meromyosin (HMM) components protruding from the surface. The whole unit is twisted so that the LMM components form coiled coils and the HMM protrude from one side at intervals of 400 Å. To form the 100-Å-diameter A filament within the muscle, six myosin "tactoids" each consisting of the four-myosin structure are packed around a central core, thought to consist of tropomyosin. The resultant structure will give the required sixfold screw arrangement of protruding knobs in the final A filament.

This structure is essentially similar to that suggested for the molluscan myofilament. The myosins would be at the surface of the filament, with paramyosin forming the central core. What we are proposing is that the central core somehow forms a continuous system independent of the myosin and actin components, and furthermore, that it is capable of undergoing a phase transition (or partial melting?). In the resting state of the muscle, the central core is plastic and can be shifted around as the myosin component moves. When the catch state is activated, the central core "freezes in" perhaps by crystallization of the paramyosin, thus maintaining the final position achieved by the myosin component during the active contractile phase. If the position of the myosin component is such that the series elastic element is stretched, then the tension so developed will be maintained by the paramyosin as long as it is crystallized.

There is some question of whether similar changes in the core are to be found in skeletal muscles, although in this context it is worthwhile recalling that tension in the isometric twitch lags behind the decay of the active state (74, 75).

SUMMARY

In this paper, the arrangement of the myofilaments which contain the fibrous proteins of muscle has been briefly reviewed. The well-known fibrous proteins, actin and myosin, are largely concerned with the performance of mechanical work at the expense of metabolic energy. A second possible function of fibrous proteins has been recently proposed by means of which mechanical energy, stored in the form of elongation of the series elastic element, can be conserved, and the economy of tension maintenance in muscles can be increased. Some workers have proposed that this increase in economy is due to peculiarities in the action of the actomyosin system, in that linkages between large and small filaments, formed during active contraction, may break at a rate much slower than the rate of breakage of actin-myosin linkages in fast relaxing systems. However, another fibrous protein, paramyosin, is found in large quantities in those molluscan muscles which are capable of maintaining tension for long periods of time without apparent fatigue or utilization of much metabolic energy. Paramyosin has properties which make it a likely candidate for the catch function, and recent experiments have indicated that many of the properties of the catch system, as it is seen in glycerinated fibers, are similar to the properties of paramyosin. Thus there is reason at present to believe that the passive maintenance of tension in at least the molluscan muscles is performed by the paramyosin system. There is, however, little evidence at present to suggest a similar function for the other fibrous proteins of the muscle group, which are similar to paramyosin in crystallizability and other aspects. Thus, tonic functions of other muscles, mainly smooth muscles, may not be of the same origin as that in molluscan muscles; this question cannot be settled until more is known about the composition of these muscles.

174   WILLIAM H. JOHNSON

ACKNOWLEDGMENTS

The author is deeply indebted to Dr. Andrew G. Szent-Györgyi, Dr. Carolyn Cohen, and Dr. Susan Lowey for the many discussions which have contributed to the author's understanding of fibrous proteins in muscle. Many of the ideas expressed in this paper have grown out of these discussions.

REFERENCES

1. Meyer, K. H., *Biochem. Z.* **214**, 253 (1929).
2. Pryor, M. G. M., *Progr. in Biophys. and Biophys. Chem.* **1**, 216 (1950).
3. Riseman, J., and Kirkwood, J., *J. Am. Chem. Soc.* **70**, 2820 (1948).
4. Morales, M., and Botts, J., *Arch. Biochem. Biophys.* **37**, 283 (1952).
5. Morales, M. F., Botts, J., Blum, J. J., and Hill, T. L., *Physiol. Revs.* **35**, 475 (1955).
6. Kuhn, W., Ramel, A., Walters, D. H., Ebner, G., and Kuhn, H. J., *Fortschr. Hochpolymer.-Forsch.* **1**, 540 (1960).
7. Katchalsky, A., *Progr. in Biophys. and Biophys. Chem.* **4**, 1 (1954).
8. Hill, T. L., *Discussion Faraday Soc.* **No.** 13, 132 (1953).
9. Huxley, H. E., *in* "The Cell" (J. Brachet and A. E. Mirsky, eds.), Vol. 4, p. 365. Academic Press, New York, 1960.
10. Huxley, H. E., and Hanson, J., *in* "The Structure and Function of Muscle" (G. H. Bourne, ed.), Vol. 1, p. 183. Academic Press, New York, 1960.
11. Huxley, A., *Progr. in Biophys. and Biophys. Chem.* **7**, 257 (1957).
12. Goodall, M., *Yale J. Biol. and Med.* **30**, 224 (1957-58).
13. Jewell, B. R., and Wilkie, D. R., *J. Physiol.* **143**, 143 (1958).
14. Hartree, W., and Hill, A. V., *J. Physiol.* **55**, 133 (1920).
15. Grutzner, P., *Ergeb. Physiol.* **3**, (2), 12 (1904).
16. Von Uexkull, J., *Z. Biol.* **58**, 305 (1912).
17. Bayliss, W., "Principles of General Physiology," 4th ed., p. 543. Longmans, Green, London and New York, 1924.
18. Hayashi, T., Rosenblueth, R., Satir, P., and Vazick, M., *Biochim. et Biophys. Acta* **28**, 1 (1958).
19. Needham, D. M., *in* "The Structure and Function of Muscle" (G. H. Bourne, ed.), Vol. 2, p. 55. Academic Press, New York, 1960.
20. Hanson, J., and Huxley, H. E., *Biochim. et Biophys. Acta* **23**, 250 (1957).
21. Szent-Györgyi, A. G., and Holtzer, H., *Biochim. et Biophys. Acta* **41**, 14 (1960).
22. Szent-Györgyi, A. G., *The Cell in Mitosis, Proc. Symposium Wayne State Univ., Detroit, 1961.* In press.
22a. Szent-Györgyi, A. G., and Johnson, W. H., "An Alternate Theory of Contraction." In press.
23. Tunik, B., and Holtzer, H., *J. Biophys. Biochem. Cytol.* **11**, 67 (1961).
24. Lowy, J., and Hanson, J., *Physiol. Revs. Suppl.* **5**, **42**, 34 (1962).
25. Oosawa, F., and Kasai, M., *J. Mol. Biol.* **4**, 10 (1962).
26. Mommaerts, W. F. M. F., *J. Biol. Chem.* **198**, 469 (1952).
26a. Asakura, S., and Oosawa, F., *Arch. Biochem. Biophys.* **87**, 273 (1960).
26b. Carlson, F. D., and Siger, A., *J. Gen. Physiol.* **44**, 33 (1960).

26c. Hayashi, T., and Rosenblueth, R., *Biochem. Biophys. Research Communs.*
27. Hanson, J., and Lowy, J., *Proc. Roy. Soc.* **B154**, 173 (1961).
28. Philpott, D. E., Kahlbrock, M., and Szent-Györgyi, A. G., *J. Ultrastructure Research* 3, 254 (1960).
29. Hanson, J., and Lowy, J., *in* "The Structure and Function of Muscle" (G. H. Bourne, ed.), Vol. 1, p. 265. Academic Press, New York, 1960.
30. Mark, J. S. T., *Anat. Record* **125**, 473 (1956).
31. Schoenberg, J. C. F., *J. Biophys. Biochem. Cytol.* 5, 609 (1958).
32. Grimestone, A. V., Horne, R. W., Pantin, C. F. A., and Robson, E. A., *Quart. J. Microscop. Sci.* **99**, 523 (1958).
33. Perry, S. V., *in* "Comparative Biochemistry" (M. Florkin and H. S. Mason, eds.), Vol. 2, p. 245. Academic Press, New York, 1960.
34. Cohen, C., and Szent-Györgyi, A. G., *Proc. Intern. Congr. Biochem., 4th Congr., Vienna (1958)* 3, 108 (1960).
35. Ruegg, J. C., *Proc. Roy. Soc.* **B154**, 209 (1961).
36. Hodge, A. J., *Revs. Modern Phys.* 31, 409 (1959).
37. Laki, K., *Nature* **193**, 269 (1962).
38. Kay, C. M., *Biochim. et Biophys. Acta* **27**, 469 (1958).
39. Doty, P., *Revs. Modern Phys.* 31, 107 (1959).
40. Hodge, A. J., *Proc. Natl. Acad. Sci. U. S.* 38, 850 (1952).
41. Simmons, N. S., Cohen, C., Szent-Györgyi, A. G., Wetlaufer, D. B., and Blout, E. R., *J. Am. Chem. Soc.* 83, 4766 (1961).
42. Riddiford, L. M., and Sheraga, H. A., *Biochemistry* 1, 95 (1962).
43. Lowey, S., and Cohen, C., *J. Mol. Biol.* 4, 293 (1962).
44. Philpott, D. E., and Szent-Györgyi, A. G., *Biochim. et Biophys. Acta* 15, 165 (1954).
45. Locker, R. H., and Schmitt, F. O., *J. Biophys. Biochem. Cytol.* 3, 889 (1957).
46. Kuhn, K., Grassman, W., and Hofman, U., *Naturwissenschaften* 44, 538 (1957).
46a. Waugh, D. F., *in* "A Biophysics Study Program" (J. L. Oncley, ed.), p. 84. Wiley, New York, 1950.
47. Hodge, A. J., *Proc. Intern. Congr. Electron Microscopy, 4th Congr.*, 2, 119 (1960).
48. Flory, P. J., *Science* **124**, 53 (1956).
49. Kominz, D. R., Saad, F., and Laki, K., *in* "Conference on Muscular Contraction, Tokyo, Committee on Muscular Chemistry of Japan," p. 118. Igaku Shoin, Ltd., Tokyo, 1958.
50. Laki, K., *J. Cellular Comp. Physiol., Suppl.* 1, 49, 249 (1957).
51. Bailey, K., and Ruegg, J. C., *Biochim. et Biophys. Acta* 42, 612 (1957).
52. Ruegg, J. C., *Proc. Roy. Soc.* **B154**, 224 (1961).
53. Johnson, W. H., Kahn, J. S., and Szent-Györgyi, A. G., *Science* **130**, 160 (1959).
54. Parnas, J., *Pflüger's Arch. ges. Physiol.* 134, 441 (1910).
55. Ritchie, A. D., "Comparative Physiology of Muscular Tissue." Cambridge Univ. Press, London and New York, 1928.
56. Jewell, B. R., *J. Physiol.* **149**, 154 (1959).
57. Johnson, W. H., and Orelup, A., in preparation.

58. Johnson, W. H., and Twarog, B. M., *J. Gen. Physiol.* **43**, 941 (1960).
59. Lowy, J., and Millman, B. M., *J. Physiol.* **149**, 68P (1960).
60. Lowy, J., and Millman, B. M., *Nature* **183**, 1730 (1959).
61. Winton, F. R., *J. Physiol.* **88**, 492 (1937).
62. Szent-Györgyi, A., *Biol. Bull.* **96**, 140 (1949).
63. Johnson, W. H., and Szent-Györgyi, A. G., *Biol. Bull.* **117**, 382 (1959).
64. Johnson, W. H., *Physiol. Revs. Suppl.* **5, 42**, 113 (1962).
65. Tahahashi, K., *Annotationes Zool. Jap.* **33**, 67 (1960).
66. Tahahashi, K., *J. Fac. Sci. Univ. Tokyo IV*, **8**, 1 (1957).
67. Twarog, B. M., *J. Cellular Comp. Physiol.* **44**, 141 (1954).
68. Ruegg, J. C., *Biochem. Biophys. Research Communs.* **6**, 24 (1961).
69. Kahn, J. S., and Johnson, W. H., *Arch. Biochem. Biophys.* **86**, 138 (1960).
70. Johnson, W. H., and Szent-Györgyi, A. G., *Federation Proc.* **21**, 316 (1962).
71. Flory, P. J., *J. Cellular Comp. Physiol., Suppl. 1*, **49**, 175 (1957).
72. Elliott, J., and Lowy, J., *J. Mol. Biol.* **3**, 41 (1961).
73. Bear, R. S., and Selby, C. C., *J. Biophys. Biochem. Cytol.* **2**, 55 (1956).
74. Ritchie, J. M., *J. Physiol.* **124**, 605 (1954).
75. Jewell, B. R., and Wilkie, D. R., *J. Physiol.* **152**, 30 (1960).
76. Hall, C. E., Jakus, M. A., and Schmitt, F. O., *J. Appl. Phys.* **16**, 459 (1945).
77. Pryor, M. G. M., *in* "Deformation and Flow in Biological Systems" (A. Frey-Wyssling, ed.), p. 191. North Holland, Amsterdam, 1952.

Subject Index

A

Acids, amino, *see also* specific amino acids,

Acids, amino,
  Bombyx mori silk, 11
  human skin, 49
  keratins, 49
  Merino 64's wool, 11
  silk fibroin, 6
  Zein, 11

Acid, aspartic,
  Bombyx mori silk, 11
  fibroin, 6
  human skin, 49
  Merino 64's wool, 11
  Merino wool, 49
  porcupine quill tip, 49
  role in charge interaction in para-
    myosin, 155
  wool fractions, 53
  Zein, 11

Acid, glutamic,
  Bombyx mori silk, 11
  fibroin, 6
  keratins, 49
  Merino 64's wool, 11
  role in band pattern of collagen,
    153
  role in charge interactions in para-
    myosin, 155
  wool fractions, 53
  Zein, 11

Actin, 140-144
  localization within myofilaments,
    142-144
  molecular properties, 143

Actomyosin, 157

Adductors, molluscan,
  filamentous structure, 144-145

Adenosine triphosphate (ATP), 142

Agents, cross-linking, 14-15

Agents, swelling, 14

Alanine,
  Bombyx mori silk, 11

  keratins, 49
  Merino 64's wool, 11
  wool fractions, 53
  Zein, 11

Albumin, egg, 6, 13

Anaphe moloneyi,
  short-chain amino acids, 8
  silk fibers, elastic recovery in air
    and water, 10
  silk fibers, extension in water, 10
  silk fibers, load-extension curves
    of, 9

Antheria mylitta,
  short-chain amino acids, 8
  silk fibers, elastic recovery in air
    and water, 10
  silk fibers, extension in water, 10
  silk fibers, load-extension curves, 9

Arginine,
  Bombyx mori silk, 11
  fibroin, 6
  groups in molecular aggregation
    of paramyosin, 156
  interaction with phosphotungstic
    acid, 153
  keratins, 49
  Merino 64's wool, 11
  wool fractions, 53
  Zein, 11

B

Bacillus subtilis, 123

Bombyx mori,
  cross section of the assembly of
    polypeptide chains, 8
  fibroin, arrangement of amino acid
    residues, 7
  short-chain amino acids, 8
  silk, amino acids, 11
  silk fibers, elastic recovery in air
    and in water, 10
  silk fibers, extension in water, 10
  silk fibers, load-extension curves, 9

Bonds,
  hydrogen, in the α-helix coil, 12

177